In Their Own Words:
Women Healed

*Testimonies of 50 Women (and their Husbands) Whose Lives
Have Been Enriched by the Medical Care, Education
and Research Efforts of the
Pope Paul VI Institute for the Study of Human Reproduction*

Edited by Jean Blair Packard

> **Descriptions of Diagnoses and Treatments by
> Thomas W. Hilgers, M.D.**

Pope Paul VI Institute Press

The term **"NaProTECHNOLOGY"** has been registered in the U.S. Patent and Trademark Office by the Pope Paul VI Institute for the Study of Human Reproduction. It can be freely used by any person or entity as long as its use reflects the medical concepts and values presented in the textbook, *The Medical and Surgical Practice of* **NaProTECHNOLOGY** (Pope Paul VI Institute Press, 2004).

Cover design by Victoria L. Sage and Jean B. Packard
Layout design by Jean Packard

ISBN 0-9744147-1-9
Library of Congress Control Number: 2004093510

With Gratitude

The assistance of many people went into this book,
and I offer my sincere appreciation to each of them:

First, of course, are the patients whose stories are
included here. Their generosity and courage in
allowing others to learn from their experiences
is truly inspirational. This book is dedicated
to each of them and their families.

Dr. Thomas Hilgers, Pope Paul VI Institute director
who generously shared his time and expertise in
contributing to this book and whose visionary
and pioneering efforts in women's reproductive health
have, with God's help, led to the healings
these women write about.

The Pope Paul VI Institute Staff, past and present, especially
those in the patient care area who are
mentioned so lovingly by many of these patients.
Additionally, Margaret Howard and Linda Cady
for lending their proofreading skills.

For all those who provide professional services in
the **CREIGHTON MODEL Fertility***Care***™ System**
and **NaProTECHNOLOGY**, whose commitment,
often with great personal, financial and professional sacrifice,
provide these healing, life-giving services.

And to my husband, Vern, and our blended family, whose love
and acceptance have helped heal my once-wounded heart.

– Jean Blair Packard, FCP –

Contents

INFERTILITY

PHYSICIAN'S COMMENTS - Thomas W. Hilgers, M.D.............59

PREVENTION OF PRE-TERM BIRTH

PREMENSTRUAL SYNDROME (PMS)

POSTPARTUM DEPRESSION (PPD)
PHYSICIAN'S COMMENTS - Thomas W. Hilgers, M.D.

NaProTECHNOLOGY for GENERAL HEALTH
PHYSICIAN'S COMMENTS - Thomas W. Hilgers, M.D.

Introduction

I cannot think of a book I would rather have my name associated with than In Their Own Words: Women Healed. I am so proud to be part of this effort and of the work of Dr. Tom Hilgers and the Pope Paul VI Institute for the Study of Human Reproduction.

The idea for this book came from the Pope Paul VI Institute nurses reading over the many patients' notes of appreciation sent to them and Dr. Hilgers over the years. Their words have had a deep impact and have been saved and treasured, and it was decided to ask some of the patients if they'd like to write a short testimony about their experiences. These stories are not written by professionals but rather by women who have struggled with various reproductive health issues.

What first amazed me was the tremendous response to our request for their testimonies. Everyone has busy lives and writing a story can be rather time-consuming and intimidating, but these women are so grateful for the help they've received that they were eager to share their stories and hope to help in any way they could.

What is striking in reading their testimonies is their courage – often in the face of physical and emotional pain – in continuing to search for the answer to their problems. You may be surprised, as I was, at the indifference they've experienced from too many physicians who don't really listen to their female patients' cries of physical and emotional pain.

This is not just a story about women from the Omaha, Nebraska area. These women live all over the United States and in Canada. It is interesting to read how they learned about the Pope Paul VI Institute and their surprise that such a place could be in the Midwest rather than on the East or West Coast.

As I shared these stories with Dr. Hilgers, he told me the deep gratitude of these women for his research, clinical and educational work was overwhelming and a bit embarrassing. He was concerned that this book would be viewed as some type of self-promotion, but that is not the goal at all. He asked me to edit out the praise, and I did to some extent but it was such an integral part of each story that to eliminate it would distort each woman's own story. Therefore, I edited as little as possible to leave it "in their own words."

My involvement began in 1978 when I met with Dr. Hilgers and later told my friends that I wanted to work for the doctor "with the fire in his eyes." I had never experienced such a visionary with total commitment to his faith and work. Since that day, I have witnessed the dedication and hard work that he and all the others involved with this effort have put into searching for answers for women in need. I've been privileged to be involved in the development of the **CREIGHTON MODEL Fertility***Care*™ **System** and **NaProTECHNOLOGY** and to observe the impact they have on women's and couples' lives. I can truly say it was one of the best decisions of my life and I've never regretted it. Every facet of my life has been influenced. In looking back I am still amazed that I served as the personal administrator to the Institute Director, Dr. Tom Hilgers, for 25 years, taught the **CREIGHTON MODEL** and currently am serving as assistant administrator for **Fertility***Care*™ **Centers of America.**

As part of the **CREIGHTON MODEL** the SPICE concept is taught. This refers to the Spiritual, Physical, Intellectual, Communicative and Emotional aspects so important to a marriage and the use of a natural method. In working on this book I came to realize that my own life has been healed in those SPICE ways. "Physically," in my late 30s, I began exhibiting the symptoms of PMS. With the help of **NaProTECHNOLOGY** my husband was able to give me progesterone shots that improved my life (and his life too, he says). Also, I know that if I had not been charting the system I would have totally ignored the early signs of adenomatous hyperplasia that my charting indicated. Eventually Dr. Hilgers performed a total hysterectomy on me for this possibly pre-cancerous condition.

Through the examples of Dr. Tom and Sue Hilgers and the other wonderful people I've worked with, my husband, Vern and I were granted annulments of our previous marriages and were married in the Catholic Church with the Hilgers as our sponsors. And because of what Vern and I have learned through the system, our "communication" is excellent and we have grown "spiritually," "intellectually" and "emotionally" very strong in our marriage.

We've seen those ripples widen to include our children from our previous marriages as well as our grandchildren – three of whom are actually Institute "Miracle Babies" – thanks to God's grace and **NaProTECHNOLOGY**.

So you may see why I believe this book is so important. I hope that the words of these contributors will provide answers as well as hope. They were written for women who are struggling with their own problems, for women's health care providers who want the best solutions for their patients, for clergy and counselors who are called upon for advice, and for all to be inspired by the deep faith and courage of these women.

The book is divided into specific sections including:

♦ **CREIGHTON MODEL Fertility*Care*™ System (CrMS)** Users
♦ Previous Miscarriage
♦ Infertility
♦ Prevention of Pre-Term Birth
♦ Premenstrual Syndrome (PMS)
♦ Postpartum Depression (PPD)
♦ **NaProTECHNOLOGY** for General Health

Each section begins with medical comments by Dr. Hilgers explaining the symptoms, diagnoses and treatments that are used. This should prove helpful as a reference if you're looking for information on a particular reproductive issue. However, I hope you'll read all of the stories. I believe they put a "face" on the work. This is a book about faith and hope and it is well worth your time. I believe you will be blessed abdundantly, as have we!

– Jean Blair Packard, FCP–

PHYSICIAN'S COMMENTS:

CREIGHTON MODEL
Fertility*Care*™ System Users (CrMS)

Thomas W. Hilgers, M.D.

The **CREIGHTON MODEL Fertility*Care*™ System** is a natural means to regulate fertility. It can be used to either achieve or avoid pregnancy and is as effective as oral contraceptives.

Developed by a team of research investigators who began their work in 1976 in St. Louis and who currently continue to investigate this system at the Pope Paul VI Institute for the Study of Human Reproduction in Omaha, Nebraska, it is a system that has literally "unlocked the code" to women's health. It is the first system to network family planning with a woman's ability to maintain and enhance her own reproductive and gynecologic health.

In 1991, a new women's health science was described. This science, called **NaProTECHNOLOGY** (Natural Procreative Technology), uses the **CREIGHTON MODEL System** for the evaluation and treatment of a whole variety of different types of women's health issues. This has all been explained in detail in the new medical textbook, ***The Medical and Surgical Practice of* NaPro-TECHNOLOGY** (Pope Paul VI Institute Press, Omaha, NE, 2004).

One of the unique features of the **CREIGHTON MODEL System** is that it allows a married couple the opportunity to know when they are either fertile or not fertile during the course of the menstrual cycle. With that information, they can select to have intercourse at times during the cycle, fulfilling their intention to either achieve or avoid pregnancy. By approaching family planning from this point of view, it challenges the couple to communicate on important areas in their lives. This communication has the potential to strengthen and bond the marriage relationship. It also has the potential of strengthening the bond of love that exists between hus-

13

band and wife and, in turn, the love that they have for their children.

The **CREIGHTON MODEL System** is a standardized modification of the Billings's Ovulation Method. It is learned through an educational process with a FertilityCare Practitioner. The couple attends a one hour introductory presentation and then individual follow-ups with the Practitioner to learn the system. For those interested in pursuing education in the **CrMS**, consult the Web site: **www.fertilitycare.org**.

The system is based upon a better understanding of the flow of cervical fluid which naturally occurs during the days leading up to the time of ovulation. This cervical fluid is essential to the sperm's survival and its penetration through the cervix so that conception can occur. At all other times during the course of the cycle, this cervical fluid is absent and telegraphs days that are not fertile during the cycle. The system is relatively simple to learn and definitely simple to use. It provides incredible feedback to a woman about her naturally occurring states of fertility and infertility and also the status of a whole variety of women's health issues. It does this through a set of "biomarkers," which have now been decoded through the research efforts of the Pope Paul VI Institute. As a result, the system has become "an authentic language of a woman's health and fertility," and the **CREIGHTON MODEL System** allows for that language to be understood and used in a practical way for family planning and issues related to women's health.

The testimonials present in this book, *In Their Own Words: Women Healed*, amplify the effect that a system such as this can have on the relationship between spouses, within the family, and toward a better understanding of women's health.

With **CrMS,** Couples Make Joint Educated Decisions
Jan Simpson

Two months before our wedding I went to visit an OB/GYN so that I could get a prescription for the birth control pill. At the time, Tom and I had never really discussed what method of birth control we should use. All of my friends who were getting married were going on the pill, so why should I be any different? After all, what other choice did I have?

After eight months on the pill and six months into our marriage, I did not have a period. I was scared that I might be pregnant. Our plan was to have at least five years together before kids. I wasn't sure what to do, so after a few tears, I decided to read the literature that came with my birth control pills. The small booklet explained exactly what the pill was doing to my body. I was sick! When I made the decision to go on the pill, it was not an educated decision. I had not even given a thought to the process of "how" it worked. I simply was following the social norm. I could not believe I was dumping these chemicals into my body. I had always taken care of myself through exercise, taking vitamins and eating relatively healthy. There was nothing natural about the pill. Tom and I definitely wanted a family and I couldn't imagine how I could chemically stop my body from ovulating and then just expect it to kick back into its natural mode when we were ready. No wonder infertility was on the rise.

I stopped taking the pill immediately and didn't even make it back to see the OB/GYN, because Tom's job was moving us from Omaha, Nebraska to Charleston, West Virginia. Once we got moved, I knew we needed to do something, but what? We both recalled our Engaged Encounter weekend and how one of the presenting couples briefly spoke about Natural Family Planning. They didn't go into any detail about the method, just simply that was what they used. We decided this was an option we needed to learn more about. We both joked about how we would be pregnant by our first anniversary if not before. I could not imagine how this would work for us because I have always had irregular cycles and I assumed this method had to be based on the Calendar/Rhythm Method.

One Sunday after church in our new parish, I found a brochure in the back of the church that talked about the **CREIGHTON MODEL**. I called the number and set up an introductory session for us to attend. This time I was determined to make an educated decision. We were greeted by a wonderful woman, Nancy Botkin, who headed up the program for the area and also happened to be a registered nurse. We learned a lot in that introductory session. First, it was a method that is successfully used by women with irregular cycles. Second, there was so much scientific research that had gone into this method that made it 99.6 percent user effective. We left that introductory session knowing that this was something we needed to pursue.

Nancy became our Practitioner who met with us individually as a couple in order to teach us the method. We truly enjoyed learning the **CREIGHTON MODEL**. We still joked that we would be pregnant by our first anniversary.

It is not a hard method to learn. The toughest part was getting through my first cycle because I had nothing to compare it to. But once the second month came, I was amazed at how all my ovulation signs returned. As each month passed, I gained more and more confidence. It was so awesome to be completely in tune with my body. I knew when I was ovulating, and best of all, I knew when my next cycle was going to start, despite being irregular. But most importantly, we were doing this together. It wasn't all on my shoulders alone. Tom took on an active role, and I am sure that he knows more about the ins and outs of the female reproductive system than most women do!

We had successfully used the method to avoid pregnancy for five years when we decided to start our family. The method had worked so well for us that we were convinced we would probably have trouble conceiving. Nine months after our first attempt at achieving pregnancy, we welcomed our first child, Timothy, into the world.

Wow, now I knew this method really did work! Almost four

years later we were blessed once again with our daughter, McKenna, who was also conceived the first time we tried for a second child. I continued to use the **CREIGHTON MODEL** while I nursed.

It is so gratifying to have one method that can be used in all stages of my reproductive life – avoiding pregnancy, achieving pregnancy, breastfeeding and even, as we were about to find out, infertility. When we tried to have a third child, it did not go as we were accustomed. I was 37 years old and my hormones had taken a nose dive. But because we knew and used the **CREIGHTON MODEL**, I feel we were ahead of the curve in treating our infertility. One week after I turned 40, I gave birth to our third child, Hope.

I only have one regret, and that is that we did not enter into our marriage with the **CREIGHTON MODEL**. All because we, together, did not make an educated decision. We came seeking this method hoping to find a means that would allow us to effectively and safely plan our family, but what we got was so much more. As a part of the FertilityCare System, we learned about SPICE (Spiritual, Physical, Intellectual, Creative/Communicative and Emotional) and how all five aspects of SPICE make up our true marital sexuality. This is the true gift of the method.

Before our son was born, we moved back to Omaha and have had the great opportunity to work with the dedicated people at Pope Paul VI Institute. I feel honored to have had Dr. Hilgers deliver all three of our children. We also still stay in touch with Nancy, our first Practitioner. Now Tom and I go to Engaged Encounter weekends as the guest speakers talking about the **CREIGHTON MODEL FertilityCare™ System**. We hope to bring a greater awareness to this wonderful method and let engaged couples know that there is another viable, reliable method to help them plan their family. We want to challenge them to make an educated decision together as a couple.

New Respect for Fertility through **CrMS**
Kristina Borngrebe

My husband, Kurt, and I got married in February of 2000 at the ages of 21 and 22 years old. Our parents suggested Natural Family Planning which we were open to, because we knew eventually we wanted to have kids and my cycles were very irregular and long. We attended the **CREIGHTON MODEL FertilityCare™ System** classes at the Pope Paul VI Institute. Charting was an interesting thing to do because my husband came to all of my appointments and learned the FertilityCare method right along with me. After all it's not just my fertility, it's ours. We are in it together, and the method allows your husband to be a part of your fertility so that he knows what's going on just as much as you do.

After a few months of charting my two week periods and 48 day cycles, we realized something was wrong. Also, even though we were trying to avoid at the time (being newlyweds) our charting looked as if we were trying to achieve. (We did not have the abstinence on fertile days down pat yet. ha-ha) Plus, I think we kind of hoped pregnancy would happen as a surprise.

After about five months, the Institute started doing the fertility tests on me including an ultrasound and blood draws and found out that I had polycystic ovarian disease. That is a condition where your body tries to ovulate but your eggs can't make it out of your ovaries, so they form what looks like pearls all over your ovaries. So having this, I do not successfully ovulate. Dr. Hilgers suggested progesterone shots to try and help the problem. Plus, the blood draws I'd had told us that my progesterone levels would drastically drop or rise from one day to the next, which is not normal. One thing I did not mention is that I suffer from depression which I had been treated for in the past with anti-depressants. When I told Dr. Hilgers this, he said it was hormonal depression. Then finding out how drastic my hormone levels were, I believed him. So began the progesterone shots on days 18, 21 and 24 of my cycle. My husband was taught to give them to me at home. After taking the shots, my periods became the normal length again and I think my cramps even got better.

After about six months of progesterone treatment, I had a talk with Dr. Hilgers about our family plans. He wanted to know how many kids we wanted to have and when we would like to start trying. I said we would like a big family of say, five kids and we would like to wait about four years to start trying when we might be more financially secure. Dr. Hilgers brought to light that with my condition I may never get five children, and because being young was to my advantage, I had a window of opportunity now that waiting four years might ruin. He suggested that if I wanted children, it would be wise to start trying in the near future and it could take as long as four years for us to get pregnant. Plus, he added, no one is financially secure. Which I can attest to this day, four years later! Anyway, he suggested that, should we wish to start trying, we would need fertility drugs. The type of drug he told me about was Clomid, a pill that makes you ovulate. I already had the "baby bug" and knew that if I mentioned the above to my husband, he would want to start trying as soon as possible too. Dr. Hilgers said that taking this pill could take a few years to work for me or it could work in as little as a few months. So I got the prescription and began taking Clomid.

Two months later, a couple of days before I was late for my period, I decided to take a pregnancy test. It came up negative. I was crushed, because I just had this feeling. After just three days of being late for that same period, I snuck over to Pope Paul VI Institute without my husband knowing and requested to take a test even though my home test had turned out negative. I never prayed so hard in my life! Two minutes later the nurse asked to see me in one of the back rooms. She said, "Congratulations you're pregnant!" I said, "Really! You're not joking?? Can I hug you?" Of course she said yes and then everything she said after that was a blur. I was on some other planet. I made an appointment to come back in a month to see the doctor and to get my first ultrasound.

That day I ended up taking a break from work and going to my husband's construction job site to surprise him with the news. I was so excited to leave my house that I tripped down my front door stairs! I cried all the way to the job site (because I was happy, not because I hurt myself ha!), and when I got there I told him that he was going to be a daddy! We hugged for a long time and right away he started the belly patting!

The first month of pregnancy was a little difficult for me because I had to be on bed rest. I was put on a pre-term labor drug and I ended up having about seven ultrasounds throughout my whole pregnancy. Dr. Hilgers takes no chances when it comes to the well-being of you and your baby during pregnancy. If there's even the slightest percentage that something could happen to your pregnancy, he has already taken precautions to prevent it. I felt very safe and taken care of at Pope Paul VI Institute. Being my first pregnancy, I was always wondering or worrying about something. The staff knew me by name when I called. They were so sweet to me. I knew I could call whenever I needed to.

I delivered Avery Spring Borngrebe November 5th 2001. She was perfectly healthy and scored the highest on the newborn tests. I was forever changed by the experience of being so blessed to have a child. After much uncertainty and my fertility problems, I am so lucky that we did the **CREIGHTON MODEL** when we did. I have met so many women since our experience that have gone years trying blindly to have children and have never tried it. It's not that difficult once you learn it, and it can save you so much heartache in the future, should you find out that you have fertility problems. My "fertility window" could have been lost had I not tried **CREIGHTON MODEL** and started trying when I did.

The birth of our daughter also changed our spiritual life and brought us back to God. She is such a miracle! Our experience getting her required us to have a lot of faith. So much so, that when we had her, we realized she was a "borrowed gift" from God and we wanted to center our lives around the Creator who gave us this precious child. Life is sacred, and we were given the privilege to raise her. Therefore, we owe the conversion back to our faith, to the Pope Paul VI Institute, and especially to Dr. Hilgers. I hold the highest regards for them and have recommended **CREIGHTON MODEL** and Dr. Hilgers to many people who are having fertility problems and to people who will benefit from practicing FertilityCare.

Two years and two months since the birth of Avery, we gave birth to our son, Aiden Joseph on January 31, 2004. He was conceived after just three months of Clomid, and continuous monthly progesterone shots. I think I have been doing the shots now for three and a half to four years. But oh how worth it!

So as you can see from my story, The **CREIGHTON MODEL FertilityCare™ System** not only made me more knowledgeable, but I found out early about my fertility problem and was given the chance to have a family where so many other women are totally oblivious to their own fertility, and try for years to get pregnant. I recommend this method with the conviction of my whole heart. I believe it is effective, safe and natural, religion friendly and will help you and your spouse to appreciate one another wholeheartedly, because you are working on this as a team. And I think it gives you much more of an appreciation of the gift of fertility and the life that can be received from it.

Radical Call to Love Embraced Through **CrMS**
Theresa Curdt

This is an account of the course that I have taken in trying to achieve pregnancies, manage an erratic cycle and a disease that affects fertility and hormonal balance. I cannot overemphasize the role of the **CREIGHTON MODEL Fertility*Care*™ System** and the science of **NaProTECHNOLOGY** in helping me feel educated and in control as much as I can be about my own health.

To begin, when I was 20 years old, I was told by telephone from a nurse at a doctor's office of my infertility diagnosis. At that time I was told that when it was time to get pregnant I would simply have to take fertility pills. That scared me; more importantly, it made me angry. I did not feel in control of my health or supported by my doctor. Why would a nurse from her office be calling me and telling me that I have a problem like this over the phone? I was not married, I was not trying to get pregnant, but I knew that I wanted to have children. I also knew that I did not want my destiny to be solely in the hands of a doctor prescribing me fertility pills; I was not involved in the equation and I was angry.

When my husband and I began our marriage preparation, we were encouraged to attend a **CREIGHTON MODEL** introductory session. At first, we were skeptical and scared. Popular culture did not put natural family planning as a viable method of planning a family. We wanted to feel in control and supported. We wanted to be educated and we wanted to know how my infertility diagnosis could be managed. We eventually wanted children, but we did not think that we were quite ready at the time that we were married.

Thankfully we attended the sessions. We were so blessed to have such a supportive healthcare staff in St. Louis, especially Diane Daly and Ann Prebil. The charting gave us knowledge in controlling/

maintaining my gynecological health. We were supported, we were educated and as a result, we were in control of our family planning. We did not solely depend on fertility medications. We worked co-operatively with my cycles to supplement with hormones, try the fertility medications and intervene surgically when necessary to rule out very realistic and scary concerns, including cancer.

It is hard to convey also the challenges of a young married couple wanting to have children and diagnostically infertile. During the two years when we were trying to achieve a pregnancy and could not, we cried; a lot. I have not mentioned the heartache that goes along with a diagnosis of infertility, and we felt isolated at times, but also had a real sense that we knew as much as we could about both of our health conditions. That was comforting. More importantly we had our faith that we were doing the most that we could to achieve a pregnancy and that the role of God as a co-Creator was ultimately part of the equation. It was a part of the equation that took us a while to understand and believe in our hearts.

We attribute this personal growth in our faith to the healthcare providers that encouraged us to pray, prayed with us and helped us to learn how to ask God to be with us on our journey. My husband and I talked and prayed together. We worked through the challenges of our infertility together. The charting helped us communicate about the sacredness of our fertility and helped us to have an even greater respect for each other during some of the most challenging times of our marriage.

Next came over two years of charting and subsequent testing with a diagnosis of polycystic ovarian disease (PCOD) with low pro-gesterone, little response to Clomid and long erratic cycles in which ovulation did not regularly occur. My fertility was complicated by findings that my husband had low sperm counts and an infection. We were devastated by the prognosis of having an even more severe diagnosis of infertility and more difficulty in achieving a pregnancy than we original thought. However, one Monday morning in April 1999, I woke up early to take yet one more pregnancy test. My hus-band, Tim, and I did not believe the positive results from the test the day before, but it was true. We were pregnant!

As a result of the knowledge that our charting provided to our health care providers and my husband and me, I was supplemented with progesterone during the first trimester. The rest of our pregnancy was normal!

After Thomas was born, my cycles were again erratic and unpredictable. I was also spotting more irregularly and did not regain any normalcy in my cycles until eight months postpartum. During this time, the charting helped me to identify exact days and the amount of spotting that was occurring. Although it was frustrating at times and worrisome, the information helped my doctor identify a cause for the spotting and also to check me for infection or other problems. I was also able to monitor times of increased fertility and ovulation as we tried to achieve another pregnancy.

In February 2001, another pregnancy test came back positive! We could not believe it! After only four months of trying to get pregnant with our second baby, we were successful! Again, I was supplemented with progesterone during the first trimester and aside from the baby being transverse and having a subsequent version and then C-Section (because the baby's foot was in the birth canal), the pregnancy was normal. Postpartum, however, irregular bleeding and difficulty establishing a normal (for me) cycle warranted a D&C. My doctor was concerned about the possibility of a piece of tissue from the placenta or even cancer causing the bleeding. Thankfully the results of the D&C came back negative. The frustration at that point was why was I bleeding and how do we control it? My charting helped us determine when to begin supplementing both progesterone and estrogen. After several months when that was not overly successful (although my cycles did begin to improve slightly), I began taking a medication that helps people with polycystic ovarian disease, called Glucophage.

Would Birth Control Pills have helped any of this? I do not think so. Despite the fact that Birth Control Pills are the prescribed treatment for PCOD, they would have masked the hormonal imbalance. The pills would have also taken control of my cycles, left me uneducated about when and how often I ovulate and left my husband and I clueless about the real challenges of trying to get pregnant with a diagnosis of PCOD.

As I close, I am so happy to report that our third baby, Michael

Cody Curdt, arrived on June 17, 2004. He weighed 7 lbs, 7 oz and was 20 inches long. We thank God for gracing us not only with the life-giving teachings of His church for married love and human life, but also with the unique gift of such knowledgeable, dedicated health professionals in our city who share our beliefs and practice medicine in full accord with these teachings.

It took us two cycles to achieve this pregnancy and again, we attribute much of our success to knowing when we ovulate and to the excellent medical management that we received. We also are so grateful that we learned to communicate and rely on each other as husband and wife and to respect our fertility (and infertility) as God had planned for us. I cannot know for sure, but I do not think I would be telling our story in this way if we had not gone to that **CREIGHTON MODEL Fertility*Care*™ System** introductory session.

We pray that more couples and health-care workers embrace the radical call to love inherent in the Church's teachings on the gift of human sexuality. It seems our troubled world needs it now more than ever.

If You Can Talk About Mucus, You can Talk about Anything
Cory Grizzle

"God won't give us what we can't handle," I told my husband, Todd, at our Engaged Encounter a few months before our wedding. He sat there quietly looking at me with an unbelieving stare, knowing exactly what I meant. We were high school sweethearts and had argued about the idea of contraception throughout the six years of our friendship and relationship, and we had agreed to disagree. When he proposed we realized we actually had to make a decision in the next six months, and so the search began.

I was a surprise pregnancy and the youngest child of six. My parents, being married in 1962 accepted and embraced the teaching of Natural Family Planning (NFP), then the Rhythm Method. My mother often said, "We don't know where she came from, but we're awfully glad she's here!" I knew the teaching of the Church against contraception (yet not fully the teaching for NFP) and was very thankful that my parents embraced it, otherwise I wouldn't be here. I did not feel that I had the ultimate authority to decide when I should have children and how many we were to bring into the world. That, I thought, should be left to God.

Todd is another story. He is the oldest of three with a brother and sister five and eight years younger. Todd is a numbers man and a planner. You've heard measure twice and cut once? He measures twice, asks a few people, measures again reads up on it, and then oh so carefully, cuts; stopping every once in a while to make sure he's doing it right. Believe it or not, it is what made me fall in love with him. When I brought up NFP as a possibility, he asked me to research it first, because we were young, we were full time students with a mortgage, a car loan, tuition and a very meager salary.

So we searched and began, of course, with our priest. What is the teaching of the Church on this subject? After a long and beautiful story, some confusing words about whether it was really the right teaching, and a pat on the back for even asking about this subject, our priest left us with a "follow your conscience" and (Praise God) the number to St. John's Mercy Medical Center's Department of NFP (now FertilityCare Services) in St. Louis.

While we attended our Engaged Encounter, this issue was at the forefront of our minds and we were determined to come away from this 72 hours with at least a better understanding of how we were going to plan our children. I knew in my heart I could not begin marriage by contracepting, but I also knew that Todd needed a scientifically proven way to plan our children.

I knew God's hand had guided us through our lives, but this weekend He was pushing us together with the right people. The two facilitating couples were strong in their faith and confident users of the **CREIGHTON MODEL Fertility*Care*™ System**. During the evening session, after the talk about parenting and planning a family, one of the activities was a round table discussion at which time each couple was to pull a question from a box and give their best shot at answering it. As soon as we pulled our question, I could feel God staring us down, wondering how we'd answer this. "How many children should you have and how do you go about planning for them?" We honestly had no clue. We shared that this was a struggle for us and the main issue we needed to resolve in the next few months.

We never really answered the question, but it was a clear sign from God that this was something incredibly important. Soon after that, we participated in the Sacrament of Reconciliation, and prayed with the Junior Facilitating Couple who had shared their story about the impact of NFP in their lives. We prayed fervently for an answer, for a peace, for someone to help us make this decision. Well, ask and ye shall receive…and receive and receive and receive. At the end of the prayer, we asked them if they would talk to us more and clear up some things for us.

In a little room late that night, after everyone had gone to bed, this couple shared with us their experience. She pulled out her chart and she had crazy cycles – two weeks, six weeks – she had infertility issues, and had two beautiful girls. They believed in this system so much she wanted to teach it and share it with everyone they knew.

I looked at her charts and listened to her confidence and knew that this is what I wanted to do. I was a perfect 28 days, like everyone thinks they are before they start charting. I knew that if this could work for cycles like hers, it would be a cakewalk for me. Todd was still not completely sold, but was willing to learn more.

Todd and I went to St. John's for an Introductory Session given by Ann Prebil. When Todd saw all of the documented research behind the effectiveness of the system, he was convinced. The pictures of the ferning patterns finally sold him. This was a system that we could use. This was a system that was proven and had solid research behind it. This system gave us both great peace. We signed up for a follow-up and went back to our lives.

Because of the length of our search for answers, we only started charting the month before our wedding: a perfect 28 days! After we were married, we used the system to postpone pregnancy. The very first month of my perfect 28-day cycle lasted until day 32. As you could probably imagine, Todd started to doubt the system. When day 33 came (and my period started), Todd heaved a huge sigh of relief. Over the next couple of months, our confidence in the system grew and we began to realize the impact it had on our marriage. We were a happy couple, we could communicate and as we have always said, if you can talk about mucus, you can talk about anything.

About this time, my mother had been mentioning to us to go to a Faith Fest being held in St. Louis, which was a day of workshops ending with keynote speaker, Scott Hahn, whom we had never heard of at the time. We stopped by a booth for the St. Louis Natural Family Planning Association and talked to the man behind the table and we signed up to get more information about the Association. One of the activities of the NFP Association was giving talks to engaged couples, explaining NFP and how it has affected their marriage. We attended a meeting of the Association and thoroughly enjoyed ourselves.

Now, me, I'm a joiner and get excited about just about anything with people who share my ideals. Todd, again the cautious one, will do quite a bit of research before we commit to anything. Surprisingly, on our way home from the meeting, I held back my urge to push him to join and before we even exited on to the highway, he mentioned, with a laugh, "Well, this would be a great way to channel my obsession with sex."

This is currently our fourth year co-chairing the Association with Matt and Debbie Muckler, and we have changed the name to the Humanae Vitae Association to more accurately reflect our mission. We have accomplished a lot for the support of couples using natural methods as well as the evangelization of the message of Humanae Vitae.

As we were plowing through our mission of evangelization, we had created two children, Gregory in 1999 and Sophie in 2001, and our lives were becoming increasingly busier. NFP was still a very good aspect of our lives, but God was telling us there was more; much more.

During one meeting in 2001, Diane Daly had suggested that we pursue an author and speaker by the name of Christopher West to come and speak on his new book, The Good News About Sex and Marriage. She had sent us a copy of his book, and it sat on my nightstand for a long time. Her enthusiasm sold me. We were looking for new things to do anyway. Sponsoring this speaker sounded pretty good. We had him set for March of 2002 and I finally got around to reading his book prior to him coming to speak. I also listened to his tape on the Theology of the Body.

As I read and listened, I became more and more enthused that he was coming. I read his book cover to cover and read paragraphs here and there to Todd.   We had a private dinner with Christopher and about 60 NFP supporters in the area. During that evening of questions and answers, I was amazed at his faith and his understanding of the Church's teaching and of his love of the beauty God has created within us. By the next day, when I had the privilege of introducing him to the audience of about 250 people, I was star struck.

Our lives changed the next day. Todd's spirituality soared. Our eyes were opened to the beauty God had created for us and within us. Lent had just begun and Todd began to pray the Rosary every day and we continued to read or listen to anything that could enrich our faith. Our lives changed. Our marriage changed. Our faith expanded. We placed a crucifix in our bedroom. We'd had a good marriage and a good faith. In a few short months it had evolved and grown to an excellent marriage and a deeper faith.

We began to enrich our faith by reading books and listening to tapes by people like Scott Hahn, Fr. John Corapi, and, of course, Christopher West. Our area is blessed to have a Catholic radio station and we listened to Catholic Answers and learned things about our faith we never realized. We started document studies and surrounded ourselves with faith-filled, God-seeking people and are amazed at the blessings we have received.

I began training to become a FertilityCare Practitioner in June of 2002 in an education program directed by Ann Prebil. Throughout the study, she kept repeating over and over, "Teach the system, teach the system." Just learning and applying the system in our lives solves so many issues, physical or mental, spiritual or marital. It makes some problems seem smaller and good marriages better. I keep repeating that mantra in my head whenever I teach.

After being away from my husband for a week during Education Phase 1, we chose to select a fertile day and conceived our third child, Bernadette. With all that I had learned during training, we knew there was no taking chances, but we were ready for more wonderful chaos in our lives.

We also began to facilitate the marriage preparation program in our parish, and at our training meeting we were asked to give one good bit of marriage advice. Without a doubt, we know that implementing NFP and specifically, the **CREIGHTON MODEL Ferti-**lity*Care*™ **System**, into any marriage will help it succeed and make a life-long covenant that much happier. This system is the root of good communication, deep respect for one another, a true under-standing of what marriage is and authentic love.

Along our journey of six years of marriage, we have learned a lot, loved a lot and lived through several ups and downs. We can now both say with certain confidence and understanding that God won't give us what we can't handle. And we also know that to whom much is given, much is expected. We credit much of our growth on the teaching of Humanae Vitae and the people in the FertilityCare Centers who have lived up to its challenges. We can only hope to spread as much of this good news as they have.

CREIGHTON MODEL has been the Perfect Choice for Our Marriage
Ann Salerno

My husband Vince and I were introduced to the **CREIGHTON MODEL FertilityCare™ System** and Pope Paul VI Institute during our preparation for marriage in 1991. During visits with our priest, Fr. Ronald Noecker, we discussed the sanctity of marriage and the precious gift of fertility from God. Vince and I decided together that natural family planning was the perfect means of respecting and appreciating our fertility within the sacrament of marriage.

We enrolled in classes for the **CREIGHTON MODEL** at Pope Paul VI Institute. The classes taught us how special and sacred our fertility was in planning our future family. We learned of the many advantages to using the method: medically safe, reliable, acceptable in our Catholic faith, inexpensive, and easy to learn. I especially loved the fact that this method is equally shared by both the husband and wife. In retrospect, this has been such a special bond in our marriage of 13 years. Vince truly respects my body and our shared responsibility of respecting our fertility.

On May 4, 1991 we received the sacrament of marriage and immediately began using the **CREIGHTON MODEL**. During those first few years of marriage we used it as a means of avoiding pregnancy in a very natural and respectful way. Linda Cady, our FertilityCare Practitioner, helped us to perfect the method and answered any questions we had.

In 1993, we decided it was time to start a family and we began using the **CREIGHTON MODEL** to achieve pregnancy. After several months of trying, we came to the realization that pregnancy was not coming easy for us. We made an appointment with Dr. Hilgers to discuss the possible reasons why we were not getting pregnant. Because we were already using the **CREIGHTON MODEL**, it was very easy for Dr. Hilgers to evaluate our situation. We already had plenty of documentation on my cycles (which, by the way, is another huge advantage to using the **CREIGHTON MODEL**). It was determined that a hormone imbalance may be causing the problem.

Amazingly, within a month of our appointment with Dr. Hilgers, we were overjoyed to learn I was pregnant with our first child! Although I was experiencing severe nausea and vomiting, the pregnancy went well. I was truly amazed at how caring and respectful the staff at Pope Paul VI Institute treated both me and the baby in my womb. It was very clear to me that they all respected the new life Vince and I created together.

On April 5, 1994, our daughter Rachel was born. She was a beautiful, healthy bundle of joy. Her first year of life was so incredible and we were sold on the gift of parenthood. In March of 1995, we decided it was time to start trying for baby number two. Within a month of trying, we were overjoyed to learn we were pregnant again. Seven weeks into the pregnancy, we learned we were expecting twins! Once again, my babies and I received the same care and respect from the staff at Pope Paul VI Institute. It was a long but exciting pregnancy. I couldn't wait for the ultrasound appointments to get a glimpse of the two babies inside of me!

On December 5, 1995, Vincent and Sarah were born 37 weeks into the pregnancy. They were beautiful and healthy. That Christmas of 1995 was so incredible for us! As we celebrated Christ's birth, Vince and I were so aware that God had blessed us with three beautiful children. The miracle of our fertility was so incredible. I was in a perpetual state of joy, relishing every moment with our three precious gifts.

Over the next two years, life became hectic. Raising three little ones was crazy enough, but Vince's mother, Nancy, had been diagnosed with a terminal illness and passed away in May of 1997. During these eventful two years, we used the **CREIGHTON MODEL** to avoid pregnancy in a loving and respectful way. We had a lot of responsibility in caring for our children and dealing with Nancy's illness and death. We learned a great deal about life during those years and realized bringing another baby into our lives would have been very challenging.

By October of 1997, our desire for another child was tugging at our hearts again. During that month we used the **CREIGHTON MODEL** to achieve a pregnancy and four weeks later we learned the exciting news; we were pregnant again! Despite teasing from friends such as, "Haven't you gotten fixed yet?" or "Don't you know what causes that?" we were overjoyed with the thought of having another baby in our family.

On July 30, 1998, our son Victor was born. His birth was so special to all of us. We were so grateful to God for blessing us with a fourth precious and healthy child. Vince and I finally felt our family was complete and we were so proud that we used our fertility in a natural and loving way to create these four beautiful children. We really felt God's hand in planning our family.

Vince and I both turned 40 within the past year and we realize our fertility is nearing the end. There are times when we desire another child and it is so incredible to know that as long as God allows, we can still have another child. So many of our friends have abruptly ended their fertility through vasectomies or tubal ligations. It is so sad to see that many of them regret these decisions. They would love to have another child, but it is not possible. Vince and I are so at peace to know that we have respected our fertility and can still try to achieve a pregnancy if we decide to and God allows us to.

The **CREIGHTON MODEL** has been such an incredible blessing to our marriage. Over the past 13 years, using it has taught us to accept our fertility as a precious gift from God. We were able to achieve and avoid pregnancy during the different phases of our marriage in a respectful and loving way. The method has been so incredibly reliable in planning the births of our children. We are so grateful to Dr. Hilgers and Pope Paul VI Institute for teaching us the **CREIGHTON MODEL** and providing medical care that respects life from the moment of conception. Vince and I strongly feel that the **CREIGHTON MODEL FertilityCare**™ **System** has been the perfect and only choice in our marriage.

PHYSICIAN'S COMMENTS:

PREVIOUS MISCARRIAGE

Thomas W. Hilgers, M.D.

When a woman experiences a miscarriage, she is often told that it is "nature's way" of handling problems; that in some way, it is a natural and normal occurrence. However, every miscarriage results because, for one reason or another, the human reproductive system is not working properly.

In cases of recurrent miscarriage, there are certain things that have been discovered as the result of the use of the **CREIGHTON MODEL System** and **NaProTECHNOLOGY** that allow for successful evaluation and treatment to be undertaken. For example, it has been found that women who have recurrent miscarriage often have limited mucus cycles. This is a biological marker that is identified with the use of the **CREIGHTON MODEL System**. It identifies a significantly reduced production in the amount of cervical mucus at the time of ovulation.

In addition to the above, it is not at all unusual for these women to experience premenstrual spotting (three or more days of spotting prior to the onset of menstruation) and/or tail-end brown bleeding (two or more days of brown or black bleeding at the end of menstruation).

These signs, observed as women track their cycles using the **CrMS**, provide meaningful information to her and to the physician regarding what the underlying problem might be. Most of the time these problems are caused by underlying hormonal dysfunctions. They can be evaluated by a thorough, targeted hormone profile and a series of ultrasound examinations done around the time of ovulation. The ovulation patterns in these women are often abnormal as well and they can be identified in this fashion.

37

An additional factor that is common in women who have recurrent miscarriage is endometriosis. This is a condition where the cells that normally line the inside of the uterus get out onto the outside of the uterus. These are called endometrial cells, thus the name endometriosis. These cells get onto the uterus, tubes, ovaries, and other tissues in the pelvic area and produce an inflammatory toxin, which is detrimental to fertility.

In studies done at the Pope Paul VI Institute, over 85 percent of patients with recurrent spontaneous abortion have been found to have endometriosis. In addition, many of these women also have underlying hormonal and ovulation-related defects as previously discussed. When these problems are adequately evaluated, the endometriosis is properly treated (we would recommend **surgical** treatment of endometriosis), and the hormone problems are properly addressed, the miscarriage risk can be reduced significantly (although it cannot be completely eliminated). The overall success rate at the Pope Paul VI Institute for a successful pregnancy following recurrent miscarriage is 80 percent (see *The Medical and Surgical Practice of* **NaProTECHNOLOGY**, Pope Paul VI Institute Press, Omaha, NE, 2004).

In addition to the above, once pregnancy occurs, it is supported with progesterone, the main hormone that supports pregnancy, and sometimes human chorionic gonadotropin (hCG). This latter hormone has also been shown to have an important effect on decreasing uterine irritability and reducing miscarriage rates.

Through **NaProTECHNOLOGY**
We have Twin Sons
Donna Biernacki

My husband and I both agree that Dr. Thomas Hilgers and the Pope Paul VI Institute are a gift and miracle for couples struggling with infertility or miscarriage. We feel very blessed to have worked with him and **NaProTECHNOLOGY**.

We had always wanted a large family, so when my daughter was one year old, I became pregnant. I had no difficulties with my first pregnancy, so we were not anticipating any problems with my second. When I was around six weeks pregnant, I began spotting and my pregnancy ended in miscarriage. My doctor told us that miscarriages were common and that we could conceive again in six months. We waited the six months that he had advised and than I became pregnant for the third time; that was in October of 2001.

I began spotting around my sixth week of pregnancy again, and we feared the worst. Once again this pregnancy ended in miscarriage. My doctor was hopeful and told us that there was most likely something wrong with the baby or it was just plain bad luck. My husband and I were not satisfied with this answer and we asked if there was any testing that we could do. He told us that there was no need to do any testing until I had three miscarriages because it probably would not happen again. He said that we did not need to wait this time to conceive and that most likely everything would be okay the next time.

In December of 2001 I became pregnant for a fourth time. My husband and I were extremely nervous that we would lose another baby. Around seven weeks into my pregnancy the spotting began, and we were devastated when we lost another baby. Our doctor told us that he would run the standard tests involving our chromosomes and blood types. We were hopeful that these tests would give us an-

39

swers, but they did not, and neither did our doctor. We were shocked when he again told us that it was most likely just "bad luck" again. All of our tests came out showing no reason for the miscarriages so he told us to try again. My husband and I left his office in shock and sorrow knowing that there had to be a reason for our losses, but we didn't know where to find them. We decided to trust our doctor, and we felt that maybe he was right, that it wouldn't happen again, because the tests showed that there was no reason for the miscarriages to be happening.

My husband and I decided to try again and became pregnant for the fifth time in March 2002. Before I became pregnant, we searched the internet and library for any information regarding repetitive miscarriages. We knew there had to be answers. When we lost our fourth child to miscarriage around my 7th week of pregnancy, we knew for certain this had nothing to do with luck. Our doctor had no answers and referred us to an infertility specialist. We wanted to find a doctor who would find the cause of my miscarriages, so we searched on our own. My sister taught Natural Family Planning and she had heard of Dr. Hilgers, so we researched his Institute.

We were very excited when we visited the Web site of Pope Paul VI Institute. We immediately knew that we wanted to work with Dr. Hilgers, and we were hopeful that he would help us. We read about **NaProTECHNOLOGY** and felt that it was an answer to our prayers. We began working with a practitioner of the **CREIGHTON MODEL FertilityCare™ System** and charted my cycles. My husband and I had practiced the Billing's Model of NFP so we were familiar with charting and we were excited that there was a doctor available to review my cycles. Dr. Hilgers look at my charts and advised us to have hormone testing done through the Institute and to schedule a visit to the Institue for a laparoscopy and ultrasound series. We were excited to begin this process and finally have answers.

We met Dr. Hilgers the day before my laparascopy was scheduled, to review my **CREIGHTON MODEL** charts and my medical history. My husband and I were amazed when Dr. Hilgers looked at my charts and told us that he felt he would find endometriosis during my laparoscopy the following day, but we were even more amazed when he turned out to be right.

Two days after my surgury we had an appointment with Dr. Hilgers to review my results from all of the tests. He told us that my endometriosis was pretty severe, but he was able to remove all of it during my laparoscopy. He also told us that endometriosis was a 50 percent cause of miscarriage. We were both very shocked because our other doctor had never mentioned this to us. Dr. Hilgers reviewed the results of my hormone profile and found that my estrogen and progesterone were low during my cycles, which could also be contributing to my miscarriages. He also found that I was Factor V Leyden positive, which is a blood clotting disorder, and that there were also some issues with my thyroid. We now had a list of four possible causes for the miscarriages. Dr. Hilgers told us he felt that we had a very good chance of having another baby because my endometriosis was taken care of and my hormones could be monitored and supported in subsequent pregnancies. Needless to say, we were very happy with the news. We discussed the progesterone and hCG shots and thyroid medications with him.

For the next couple of months Dr. Hilgers monitored my hormones until he felt they could sustain a pregnancy. After two months, he told us that he felt we could conceive. We were excited but nervous because of the pain experienced with our four miscarriages.

I became pregnant in October 2002 for a sixth time. We were very supported from Dr. Hilgers and the Institute during this pregnancy. They monitored my hormone levels and ordered an ultrasound at six weeks. All of my hormone levels had been great and I had not experienced any spotting so we were looking forward to seeing a heartbeat; but instead, we saw TWO heartbeats! Our doctor informed us that I was carrying two healthy babies and that everything looked great. We were so surprised and felt so blessed with the news. Dr. Hilgers continued to monitor my hormone levels long distance and supported me through my entire pregnancy. I had a wonderful pregnancy with no complications.

On June 24, 2003, I gave birth to two beautiful baby boys, Thomas and James. (We felt the least we could do was name one of our sons after Dr. Thomas Hilgers.) Everyday when we look at our boys we are so thankful for the treatment that we received from Dr. Hilgers and **NaProTECHNOLOGY.**

At the Pope Paul VI Institute
Hope was Restored
Lori Kuhfahl

Miscarriage! This is a word that I have become painfully familiar with in my life. In total, I have had four. My first was when I was very young and had no real concept of what motherhood was all about. My second was after I had successfully delivered two boys. This time the loss was much more difficult. It happened on my 29th birthday, which was also the day before Thanksgiving. The experience was heart-wrenching. They told me my baby was dead after doing an ultrasound in the hospital. The ultrasound tech was not happy to have been called into work on a holiday weekend. The doctor came in and told me that I had two choices, either be admitted to the hospital now, or go home and let nature take its course. My quick decision was to stay at the hospital and get things taken care of right away. I was twelve weeks pregnant at the time and had to go through labor, and when my body was ready, the doctor did a D&C. I was able to go home Thanksgiving morning, numb and very devastated. I felt so empty inside. For the sake of my young family, I had to pick myself up and carry on with the Thanksgiving holiday. The people around me were feeling festive and happy, but I felt devastated and alone.

Over the next few days, my well-meaning friends and family either did not acknowledge the loss at all, or commented on the fact that I was "young and could have more children" or "miscarriage happens when a baby is not healthy or normal." These were things that I really did not care to hear.

Months went by while I walked around with a heavy heart. I was frightened at the though of trying for another baby. I never wanted to feel loss like this again. But, about a year later, my husband and I received the miraculous news that I was pregnant again. This time I was going to have twins.

This pregnancy carried out without any significant problems, and in April of 1992, my twin boys were brought into this world. I felt complete. Four boys! What a blessed, busy house I had. What more could I ask of God?

Over the next seven years, my husband and I lovingly raised our family. We moved to Wahoo, Nebraska, which seemed to be such a blessing. We settled into a Catholic church, school and a very strong circle of friends who became like family to me.

My husband and I rarely spoke of trying for another child, but we did nothing to prevent another pregnancy. We just figured that this was the family God wanted us to have. We were surprised, yet elated, to find out in the spring of 1999 that we would be having a millennium baby, due late December of 1999 or early January 2000. We kept this news to ourselves since I had experienced two miscarriages already. We wanted to wait until we felt confident that this baby was really going to be born. Then one day, my best friend asked me to lunch. It was there that she shared with me that she was expecting her sixth child. I could not hold my news in any longer, and I very excitedly told her that I was also expecting. Our babies were due within a couple days of each other. I was absolutely bursting with joy. Our doctors' appointments came next. She went to her appointment and I went to mine. We then met for lunch to talk about what we both found out. It was just so fun to share this time with my best friend.

Several weeks went by and I went back for a second doctor's appointment and ultrasound. This is where the trouble began. My baby's heartbeat was extremely slow, and seemed to be very irregular. My doctor sent me to a radiologist right away to get a more detailed ultrasound. It was at this ultrasound that my baby's heartbeat had stopped. I lay on the ultrasound table praying to God, and begging the Virgin Mary to intercede on my behalf, to save my baby. There she was, a perfectly developed baby inside of me, but had no heartbeat. It was then that I was again given two choices, either check in to the hospital for labor and eventual D&C or go home and let nature take its course.

This time, I decided to go home. I felt like I was in a different place in my life spiritually, and if I prayed hard enough, my heart would heal quickly. I also knew that my friends would be there for me, to help me through this devastating time. I just knew I would not be alone. I again walked through life feeling very numb. My baby was no longer living, and I had to wait for my body to realize it. After waiting about a week, my body began to show signs of miscarriage. After a very painful night, a D&C was again performed.

I was so devastated. Very early on, I felt like this time, this loss was really going to change my whole life, and it did just that. Through this loss, I also lost my best friend, because she felt it would be painful for me to be around her and her healthy pregnancy. So she stayed away. I was doubly devastated, confused and angry.

Two months after this, I had another positive pregnancy test. I sought the counsel of a very wise priest friend of mine, who advised me to seek help at the Pope Paul VI Institute. I also realized through my own miscarriage, that I needed a doctor and a clinic where spirituality was extremely important. If I was going to have to accept what could potentially happen with this pregnancy, I was going to have to be surrounded by people who believed that God has a plan, and I needed to lean on Him in times of trouble. It was at the Pope Paul VI Institute, that I learned the fate of this most recent baby. They told me that this pregnancy was not going to progress and I needed to go home and prepare myself for yet another miscarriage.

At my appointment following this fourth miscarriage, I told the doctor that I felt completely defeated. I did not think I could physically or emotionally go through this ever again. The staff at the Institute convinced me to just go through the classes to learn about the **CREIGHTON MODEL FertilityCare™ System** and eventually they may be able to help me to not only achieve another pregnancy but possibly to carry to full term. I went home and thought about this long and hard and then decided to enroll in classes.

I knew in my heart that the Pope Paul VI Institute's work was the best chance I had of successfully adding to our family. I did everything they told me to do. I went through my FertilityCare classes, charted diligently and got my blood drawn every other day for what seemed like an eternity. Through all of this, my fear began to turn to hope. Dr. Hilgers and his staff counseled me and soon I became less and less frightened. Six months later, my husband was working on a parish retreat. I felt "different" for some reason and decided to do a home pregnancy test. It was positive. I can remember my heart racing – happy – excited – scared.

I called Dr. Hilgers at home to tell him the news and he very calmly told me exactly what to do. Over the previous months, they found I had somewhat of a progesterone problem. If I could keep my progesterone at a healthy level, my pregnancy should progress. In the next couple of days, I had a very early ultrasound where we saw a clear and healthy heartbeat.

Over the next nine months my body struggled to maintain good progesterone levels. I felt confident that the staff at the Institute were keeping a watchful eye on things and would do whatever was humanly possible to maintain my pregnancy. I felt I was doing the very best that I could for my unborn baby. There were even times when the nurse had trouble drawing my blood. I would hear her quietly saying a prayer for God to guide her through the blood draw. All of these things made me feel so much more at ease.

On November 16, 2000, Celia Elizabeth-Rose Kuhfahl was born to an emotional mom and dad, not to mention the four Kuhfahl brothers who were anxiously awaiting her arrival, excited beyond words.

When Celia was 18 months old, we found out I was expecting once again. With Dr. Hilgers and his staff keeping watch over me and my baby once again, they diligently looked over my lab results every other week and adjusted my progesterone shots as needed. On August 31, 2002, Isaiah Michael Kuhfahl joined our family.

I really believe in my heart that without Dr. Hilgers and the Pope Paul VI Institute, I would not have my two latest successes (Celia and Isaiah). My priest friend once said, "Mothers are very fortunate people. In childbirth, they directly assist God in making a miracle happen." I would have to add that I think the knowledge God has given Dr. Hilgers through his research also directly assists in the miracle making. The four souls that God has in heaven that once touched my life have truly changed my life. They pointed me in the direction of the Pope Paul VI Institute where hope was restored and for me; miracles have happened.

Life is Very Full with Four Kids
Katie Hudek

Overjoyed at becoming pregnant, I was like many other first-time, newly pregnant women. I was full of hope and planning for a wonderful future. A baby! Our baby! On a Sunday afternoon when I was ten weeks pregnant I started spotting. Surely this would stop. It didn't. When I called the doctor, he said I was probably miscarrying. The following day I went in for an ultrasound to be sure the miscarriage was complete. The doctor stated that he didn't know why the baby died, but it was probably for the best as there was likely something wrong with it. These words weren't very consoling, and I came to find out later through the Pope Paul VI Institute that they were just plain wrong.

When I became pregnant again, we told no one. I returned to my doctor who said my blood count was high, so at 11 weeks, I packed for a family reunion. The next day en route to our vacation destination, I began to spot. A long-distance phone call to the doctor was placed and he said not to worry as my count was high. The bleeding became heavier and I went to the hospital. They said I was miscarrying again. Sadness, fear, and frustration swirled in my head. Four days later I went to the emergency room, as the pain was so intense. Finally the miscarriage was over. The doctor said the same words as last time and that they would not investigate the cause of the miscarriages until I had experienced three of them. I was not going to wait around for that.

I don't know exactly how I came upon the Pope Paul VI Institute. After experiencing two heart-wrenching miscarriages (is there any other kind?), I was highly motivated to seek some answers. Almost immediately upon beginning at the Pope Paul VI Institute I became pregnant. This was no surprise as getting pregnant was not my problem; staying pregnant was. I started receiving progesterone and hCG shots. At nine weeks, I was so worried I was going to miscarry again; I shared this concern with Dr. Dixon and he sent me right down to get an ultrasound. There was the baby's heartbeat right before my eyes. He probably never knew how much seeing my baby on that screen helped ease my mind. I continued with the progesterone shots for the duration of the pregnancy and in June of 1993, our first born daughter entered this world in the most amazing, natural way. Our baby was finally here, our hopes finally realized through the work of Dr. Hilgers and his staff.

Two years later, I became pregnant again, and with the help of progesterone and hCG shots over the course of the entire pregnancy, our second child, a son, was born,

For a variety of reasons that in hindsight seem ludicrous, we stopped going to the Pope Paul VI Institute and instead chose to go to a different OB/GYN. I shared my past history with this doctor and he told me that the use of progesterone after the first trimester is actually harmful to the fetus. He went on to say there was no reason I couldn't have another healthy baby. So I became pregnant and I was put on progesterone suppositories, which I remembered hearing at the Pope Paul VI Institute were not as effective as the shots. At 12 weeks, I was told to stop their use. I took them for two more weeks anyway. Everything seemed to be going along well and I went in for my first routine ultrasound at 21 weeks. There was no heartbeat. The baby had died. You cannot imagine my shock, anger, frustration, sadness and guilt. Based on the baby's measurements, they believed the baby died at 19 weeks and called it a miscarriage.

I had experienced two previous miscarriages and this loss was nothing like those. This was a hundred times worse. Because the baby was too large to pass on its own, I was scheduled to go to the hospital two days later for labor and delivery. They gave me drugs to soften my cervix and drugs to induce labor. After almost 24 hours I delivered a very small, dead baby. We named him Gerard. I held him in my arms and counted ten fingers and ten toes and stared into the bluest eyes I'd ever seen. It was an incredibly awful experience. To hand Gerard over to the nurse and not be able to take him home was so painful. And it was all so preventable! To think this baby could have been born full term and alive had I stayed at the Pope Paul VI

Institute was overwhelming.

The doctor gave no reasons for the baby's death. All the tests they ran didn't indicate any problems. But it doesn't take a rocket scientist to figure out that three pregnancies without progesterone ended in miscarriage and two pregnancies with progesterone produced healthy babies. We couldn't get back to the Pope Paul VI Institute fast enough.

One year later, our third child, a daughter, was born and three years later, our fourth child, a son was born. Progesterone and hCG shots were used throughout both pregnancies.

I write this as our four month old baby sits contentedly in his swing, our three year old pounds on play dough and our seven year old and ten year old attend school. Life is very full with four kids. It is impossible to imagine where I might be right now if it hadn't been for Dr. Hilgers and his staff at the Pope Paul VI Institute. We are so grateful to all the incredibly caring people we met there.

We want Women to Know There are Other Options Available
Debbie Lutgen

I became pregnant for the first time in April of 1996. I was 40 years old. My husband, Dennis, and I had been married three years. We both had waited until later in life to marry and, like many couples, never anticipated any problems having children. When we received the phone call confirming our first pregnancy, I wasn't sure how I felt. I was a little excited, but more anxious, already wondering how I was going to handle a pregnancy and becoming a mother. Dennis was very excited. I wasn't pregnant long, miscarrying six weeks later.

I became pregnant for the second time that same year in September. My doctor told me the chances of a second miscarriage were slim, so I didn't worry. I was very excited. That time I was pregnant for three months. When we went for my second doctor's appointment, there was no heartbeat. At thirteen weeks I had miscarried again and had a D&C. I was devastated.

My third pregnancy was in February of the following year, just two months after my D&C. I was pregnant eleven weeks. I had another D&C in April of that year.

After three miscarriages, each one not long after the other, my emotions were overwhelming. I wanted a baby so badly that at times I felt a physical pain. The summer of 1997 was an incredibly hard one for me. I didn't realize I was going through depression. Every morning I would tell myself that today would be different and everything would be okay. I suffered (and my husband, family and friends did too!) for seven months until a trip to the hospital emergency room one evening ended in my being treated for clinical depression.

In January of 1998, the following year, I was pregnant again. My fourth miscarriage happened at seven weeks. During this whole time, my OB/GYN doctor never referred me to a specialist of any kind. During one of the pregnancies he did put me on progesterone suppositories, but that was ineffective. I did not have an adequate understanding of my problems in order to seek out a specialist on my own. I remember asking my doctor if he had other patients who'd had as many losses, trying to determine for myself if this was normal. He stated he did not, but he did not suggest any other course of action.

In my own heart, I wanted to try one more pregnancy so that I wouldn't have any regrets about not trying hard enough to have a child. I became pregnant in November of 1998, my fifth pregnancy within a two-year period.

This time I stayed pregnant! I had no problems and no special treatments. I enjoyed my pregnancy. I went into labor at 35 weeks, and within two hours of being admitted to the hospital, our little boy was born by emergency cesarean section. It all happened so fast! David Leon Lutgen, born August 1, 1999, was premature, but he never had any health problems.

When David was a year old, I became pregnant, miscarried and became pregnant again that same year for the sixth time. I was ready to give up, just so very thankful that God had given us one child... UNTIL I made a trip to Wal-Mart in Lincoln, Nebraska, several months after my last miscarriage. This is my Wal-Mart story.

My little boy and I were at Wal-Mart at the front of the store; I was watching him while he played on the mechanical horse. There were several children playing next to him and a lady standing nearby. I asked her if they were ALL her children, and she said yes. I said "You have been blessed to have so many children." She told me it had not been easy and that she had also had several miscarriages. Her story was similar to mine. She told me she had found a doctor in Omaha who had helped her "get pregnant" and "stay pregnant." We only talked for about five minutes that day, but before she left, I asked if she might give me the name of this doctor. She had his card in her purse and passed along his name and phone number. It was Dr. Tom Hilgers.

I was skeptical. I told Dennis about my encounter with the "Wal-Mart lady" as I now call her, and about the doctor in Omaha. Dennis thought we should call him, but I wasn't so sure. We knew nothing about him. Besides, I didn't know if I wanted to go through the emotional trauma of trying to have another baby. However, we wanted to have more children, so after about four weeks, I called Dr. Hilgers's office and made an appointment.

Dennis and I met with Dr. Hilgers in June of 2000. We knew when we walked into his office that this must be a very qualified, competent doctor—there were photographs in the waiting room of him shaking hands with the Pope—and we learned he was the Director of the Pope Paul VI Institute! We were impressed! In that first consultation, after hearing our story and being told my medical history, Dr. Hilgers told us we had about a 70 percent chance of having a baby. He told us about "charting" and explained about hormones. By the time Dennis and I left his office, we were in awe! On the drive home we were so excited! We felt like we had just made a monumental discovery! We wondered why other doctors didn't offer this information to their patients. Dr. Hilgers's approach made so much sense to us and his treatments seemed so "natural."

The following week we met with an instructor of the **CREIGHTON MODEL FertilityCare™ System** in Salina, Kansas. After reviewing the manual, having her explain the charting process and watching a short film explaining the importance of hormone balance during a woman's cycle, we were amazed! I never knew that I could know so much about my own body, AND, in addition, through the charting process, determine where I was at any given point in my cycle. I, once again, could not understand why OB/GYN doctors were not giving this information to their patients.

I started charting right away and started the blood work Dr. Hilgers had ordered. I had ultrasounds performed, as he requested, and I had the laparoscopic surgery.

Six months later, I had completed all of the tests and Dr. Hilgers had evaluated my file. He told me I was very low on progesterone during certain times of my cycle, that I had a hormone imbalance, and that the endometriosis found during the operation had been surgically eliminated. He said all of these conditions could be causes of my miscarriages and that we were now ready for a pregnancy. I became pregnant the second cycle. The charting really worked for us!! Dr. Hilgers put me on progesterone and hCG injections immediately. Dennis gave me two injections twice a week. I had monthly visits with my family doctor in Beloit, Kansas but continued to be monitored by the Institute throughout my pregnancy. Via blood samples mailed to the office every two weeks, Dr. Hilgers monitored my progesterone levels and increased or decreased the amount accordingly. I went to his office as he requested for ultrasounds. I have never been monitored so closely by a doctor. One of his nurses told me one time that they and Dr. Hilgers wanted to keep me pregnant just as much as I wanted to stay pregnant!

In my fifth month I was in Dr. Hilgers's office for an ultrasound. We were so excited because we found out we were having a little girl! Our excitement was short-lived. About twenty minutes later as we sat in the examining room with Dr. Hilgers, he informed us that the ultrasound had showed a shortening of the cervix, meaning I had started going into premature labor. He told us that in order to keep me from delivering, he would have to do an emergency cervical cerclage and quickly explained the procedure to us. This was about 4:00 in the afternoon. By 5:30 that afternoon we had been checked into the hospital and I had already had surgery! He did not waste any time!! For the remainder of my pregnancy I received antibiotics given intravenously through a drip twice a week to treat a low-grade uterine infection and Terbutaline tablets taken every four hours to prevent contractions. The intravenous antibiotics were the worst part, and sometimes it was hard to get up at 4:00 a.m. to take the Terbutaline; but I would go through it all again for the outcome we achieved! Our little girl, Amy Margaret Lutgen, was born September 3, 2002 (just 15 months after our initial consultation with Dr. Hilgers), delivered via a scheduled C-section at 37 weeks by my doctor in Beloit. She was perfectly healthy.

We are very thankful to Dr. Hilgers for our little girl's life. I feel certain that if I had been seeing a regular OB/GYN, none of the precautions would have been prescribed and I quite possibly would have miscarried again.

I remember thinking several times during my pregnancy that Dr. Hilgers was being a bit over-cautious. But knowing what I do now, I don't believe he is as over-cautious as he is just very thorough in the treatment of his patients!

We are thankful every day for the gifts God has given us in David and Amy. They are both miracles. And we are also thankful for our six little angels that are with Him now in Heaven. We believe and know without a doubt that we are not in control of our own child-bearing and in the end God has the final word. God is the only reason David is here. In His infinite wisdom, He may have intervened several times to keep David in the womb long enough to be born healthy. We believe God used Dr. Hilgers as His instrument in giving us Amy.

When we went for our initial consultation with Dr. Hilgers, I told him I didn't know if we needed to be talking with him, because we believed that if God wanted us to have children He would give them to us, one way or another. He replied, "If you have a clogged sink, are you just going to pray about it and hope it starts working, or are you also going to call a plumber?" Dr. Hilgers explained that he is not playing God; he is just being used to bring about God's plan. We know Dr. Hilgers does not have all the answers and he is not the one who produces life; but we also believe that God has given him wisdom on certain issues that is meant to be shared. Our hope and prayer is that the information and research to which Dr. Hilgers has devoted his life's work will be made available to all women through their doctors. We want women to know there are other options available! We wish we had known about the Institute's research sooner, but the important thing is that we know it now and can pass it along to others, which we do every chance we get!

Best Case Scenario Result of Institute's Help
Anonymous

Looking back, of the family and friends I have known throughout the years, none can empathize, let alone sympathize, with my complex fertility and reproductive history. I have no doubt that this is the overwhelming consensus of most women, who like myself, have struggled for years to find some type of normalcy. Today, however, I can positively relate to you that it has been through the care of Dr. Hilgers, and by means of his reproductive technology, knowledge, and expertise, a best-case scenario has resulted.

My husband and I have used the **CREIGHTON MODEL FertilityCare™ System** for all of our married life. To its credit, we have been richly blessed with four children. Our challenges first began when we were trying to conceive our second child. Over the next nine years we experienced seven miscarriages at varying stages of gestation. In addition to this, each time we were able to conceive; complications arose in the earliest stages. There had not been one pregnancy, excepting the first, where heavy bleeding, hormonal deficiencies, and low levels of amniotic fluid were present. Most, if not all, doctors prescribed bed rest for me. They were not educated or willing to educate themselves for my baby and me. When faced with these situations, other than prescribing bed rest, most doctors promoted or suggested terminating the pregnancy. After the birth of our fourth child, who was born in her 27th week because of the problems mentioned above, we began to expect that we would find no answer to the problems.

Despite a tireless effort to seek out specialists to help us with deciphering and solving these problems, we continually ended up back where we had begun. Finally, a family practice doctor, who is well experienced with the **CREIGHTON MODEL**, recommended we consult Dr. Hilgers in Omaha, Nebraska. Within a month's time,

I had compiled and mailed my complicated medical files to him. After the initial review of my history, Dr. Hilgers brought numerous issues and information forth which had never been discussed or considered before by other doctors. Dr. Hilgers had a good overview of my past because we had been using the **CREIGHTON MODEL**, and I had kept clear and accurate records of my menstrual cycles. He then recommended a clear treatment plan, and I was given direction on a monthly basis. Furthermore, the medications and subsequent lab results were monitored closely, and he could now evaluate changes in my hormonal levels.

As these hormones were monitored and regulated, not only did I begin to feel an improvement in my general health, but we were also preparing my body to accept a new life. After eight months of treatment, we conceived in June of 2003. Dr. Hilgers' care has been a wonderful experience, despite living 400 miles away from his Institute. Thus far, we have experienced a healthy pregnancy through his help. Primarily, the qualities that I feel have made this pregnancy and its care so different from previous experiences are as follows:

1. The careful and consistent monitoring of my symptoms, blood work, and medications on a weekly basis.
2. The understanding of hormonal monitoring and support in pregnancy as logical and necessary for some patients.
3. Though my pregnancies have been considered high-risk, the care given with this pregnancy differs and does not follow secular mainstream obstetric protocol in extreme ways.

As of now, we are six weeks away from our anticipated due date. I have had what I consider an exceptional pregnancy considering my past, and have not experienced the conditions which where part of previous pregnancies. I continually find that I am both surprised and amazed that such a reversal of health problems could be possible. Without doubt, the success thus far can be contributed solely to Dr. Hilgers and his mastery in understanding a woman's reproductive health. Furthermore, the knowledge and care provided by his staff has been a tremendous blessing. On behalf of my husband and family, we owe a life-long debt of gratitude and thanks, and anxiously anticipate holding our new baby for the first time.

PHYSICIAN'S COMMENTS:

INFERTILITY

Thomas W. Hilgers, M.D.

The number of women who are experiencing infertility in the United States has significantly increased over the last 20 years. Infertility is generally defined as the inability to achieve a pregnancy (with the use of random intercourse) over a 12 month period of time. All infertility is the result of underlying disease.

The CREIGHTON MODEL System (CrMS), with its focus on the better understanding of human fertility, also allows for a better evaluation and treatment plan to be developed for women who experience infertility problems. Such conditions as limited mucus cycles, premenstrual spotting, tail-end brown bleeding, long and irregular cycles, and in some cases, the complete absence of menstruation and ovulation, are findings observed in women with infertility.

What the **CrMS** has introduced into the evaluation of infertility is truly "the missing link" in infertility evaluation and treatment. Over the last 30 years, the major emphasis in the approach of infertility treatment has been the use of artificial reproductive technologies. In these approaches, the underlying cause is "jumped over" and ignored. Since conception is coordinated in an artificial fashion, it is thought that the natural underlying fertility problem can be ignored. Because of this approach, modern management of infertility reaches only 20 to 30 percent success rates. In fact, *in vitro* fertilization, which is the major form of artificial reproductive technology, **actually helps less than 1 percent of infertile couples in the United States on a yearly basis**.

NaProTECHNOLOGY and the **CREIGHTON MODEL System** have refocused the energies in infertility on establishing a sound diagnosis of the underlying problem and then treating it successfully. This is usually done first of all, by tracking one's cycles using the **CrMS** and looking for the various biomarkers that might indicate an abnormality. Then, an underlying hormonal evaluation and ultrasound study is done, followed by a diagnostic laparoscopy and selective hysterosalpingogram. All of these tests will almost always determine the underlying cause.

These causes then have specific forms of treatment that can be applied. The success of these programs ranges from 30 percent (with very severe pelvic adhesive disease and occlusion of the fallopian tubes) to a high of 80 to 85 percent in women with polycystic ovarian disease and chronic anovulation. In fact, **NaProTECHNOLOGY** has now been shown to be 1.4 to 2.8 times more successful than the current artificial reproductive technologies. In addition, the underlying diseases are not ignored; they are treated.

Institute is a Bastion of Hope and Reaffirmation
Deborah J. Colloton

I write as a joyfully pregnant, 38-year-old expectant mother. And all thanks goes to Dr. Thomas Hilgers and the Pope Paul VI Institute. I could not thank Dr. Hilgers enough not only for his medical excellence, but for offering health care consistent with the principles of Humanae Vitae. And I could not praise the staff of the Institute more highly for their kindness, responsiveness and professionalism. Having been a patient of the Institute now for over one year, I can say without qualification that the care and attention I have received is superior and, in fact, without equal among the many institutions where I have been treated previously.

BACKGROUND

The journey to where I am today was neither short nor easy. My husband and I had tried to conceive for two-and-a-half-years before I found out about the Pope Paul VI Institute. To my surprise, I found medical help in Omaha, Nebraska, that was not offered to me by major medical institutions on the East Coast. Also to my surprise, it was my adopted Catholic faith that led me to the best medical care available for reproductive health problems.

During the two-and-a-half-year period when my husband and I were trying to conceive, I was diagnosed with Graves disease. Doctors I consulted about my apparent fertility problems pointed to the Graves disease as the culprit. Friends and family pointed to a harried schedule of constant travel and work as a possible source of my inability to conceive. All of this made sense, and I figured once I settled down and completed treatment for Graves disease that all would be well. It wasn't. Following my treatment, I was still unable to conceive. My then OB/GYN began a piecemeal approach to look for possible problems with my reproductive system. A consult with an IVF specialist was recommended as something I should consider.

Out of frustration and because of my opposition to artificial procreation, I decided to research options on the Internet. I found the Pope Paul VI Institute web page and contacted them. What followed was not only a thorough and professional evaluation of my reproductive health, but treatment for more than one health problem and, happily, my pregnancy. I can only wish this high level of health care for all women suffering from fertility problems.

DIAGNOSIS

I contacted the Pope Paul VI Institute in February 2003, hoping for an immediate appointment with Dr. Hilgers. My hopes were dashed when I was told that I had to complete two months of "NaProTracking" (charting of my monthly cycles), and later, I learned, a month-long hormone study before scheduling an appointment. But I soon understood and appreciated why this is so. Unlike other doctors I have consulted—and doctors my family and friends have consulted—Dr. Hilgers takes a thorough approach to assessing a woman's reproductive health. He follows this common sense wisdom: if a couple is not conceiving, there is a medical problem that should be identified and treated. This is called a "disease-based approach." A proper diagnosis can take months. It sounds obvious, but it does not seem to be the normal standard of care in reproductive medicine today! This thorough approach is especially critical for women for whom age is an issue: I wasted years of time without proper diagnosis of my reproductive problems. Lesson learned: don't assume just because one reason for infertility has been posited, or even identified, that another reason or reasons do not exist. Dr. Hilgers's approach is the best because he provides a full evaluation of a woman's entire reproductive system.

Before even meeting me, Dr. Hilgers required information that most OB/GYNs NEVER collect: the NaProTracking of my monthly cycles and a hormone study that consisted of ten blood draws over a one-month period. I was put in touch with a local nurse trained in the **CREIGHTON MODEL FertilityCare™ System** and she ensured that I completed accurate charting of my monthly cycles. Based on this information and a short, written medical history I provided to Dr.

Hilgers, he was able to tell me before we ever even met that I likely had endometriosis and a hormonal abnormality. This surprised me, since neither of these conditions had ever been raised by the doctors who had been treating me for years previously. In fact, I had inquired of half a dozen doctors, over a period of almost 20 years, about endometriosis. Every time I inquired about endometriosis, I was brushed off; my OB/GYNs would prescribe painkillers, or the birth control pill to manage the pain.

When I became engaged in 1999, I sought out a top OB/GYN in New York City (where I lived at the time) specifically to ask about endometriosis, as I had recently read that it had implications for fertility. I explained my symptoms and my concerns about fertility to this doctor—a big muckety-muck in the city; he patted me gently and essentially escorted me out of his office with a new prescription for painkillers. "But, I read an article that says the only way this can be diagnosed is through laparoscopic surgery" (which is true), I told him. "Surgery!" he barked, "you don't need surgery!" He told me I was in great health and had nothing to worry about. I felt so stupid; I thought endometriosis must be something far worse and more remote than I had understood, and of course there was no way I had it.

I put it completely out of my head until the day of my first appointment with Dr. Hilgers in June 2003. Dr. Hilgers began our appointment by saying, "I'll bet Fort Knox that you have endometriosis." (I told Dr. Hilgers about the muckety-muck and he nodded—"happens all the time.") Dr. Hilgers spent an hour with me that day, reviewing the material I had provided and outlining a course of action for treatment. In addition to the suspected endometriosis, he noted that I had low levels of pre-ovulation estrogen (indicated by both my **CREIGHTON MODEL** charts and my hormone study).

TREATMENT

My treatment began the day after my first appointment with Dr. Hilgers. I was scheduled to be in Omaha for about two weeks in order for a full evaluation to be completed. This included laparoscopic surgery, during which Dr. Hilgers was able to examine my reproductive system, and treat the endometriosis that he confirmed

I had. The treatment for endometriosis, particularly among women who have fertility concerns, is laser surgery. I was lucky to be among the approximately 60 percent of patients for whom Dr. Hilgers can complete laser surgery during the initial laparoscopic procedure. Dr. Hilgers videotapes his surgeries and later reviews the procedure with patients. The lasering literally vaporizes the troublesome endometrial sites.

During the same surgery, Dr. Hilgers performed a selective hysterosalpingogram; this is the test where a dye is injected through the fallopian tubes to determine whether they are completely open or blocked. I'd had a hysterosalpingogram performed in New York six months prior to my Omaha visit and was told everything was clear and normal. But Dr. Hilgers performs a selective hysterosalpingogram, which is a more sophisticated version of the same test. He calibrates the pressure with which the dye is injected, to get a better idea of whether there is any blockage. The results of my selective hysterosalpingogram showed that there WAS some blockage in both fallopian tubes. Though the blockage likely was not sufficient to prevent pregnancy, it certainly would not help achieve it, and it could have been an impediment to a fertilized egg traveling back through the fallopian tubes on its way to the uterus for implantation. Trapping the fertilized egg in the fallopian tubes would cause an ectopic pregnancy. Dr. Hilgers treated the partial blockage of my fallopian tubes.

In addition to the laparoscopic surgery, I underwent daily vaginal ultrasounds as part of my two-week stay in Omaha. The ultrasound technician charted the progress of all developing egg follicles in my ovaries and was able to determine that I did ovulate. By measuring the size of the egg follicle that ruptured, the technician found that I had "premature follicle rupture." When the egg follicle ruptures prematurely, it is far less likely to be able to be fertilized and more likely to result in miscarriage if it does become fertilized. This finding was consistent with the results of my hormone study that showed low estrogen prior to ovulation; it is estrogen that supports proper egg follicle development.

Following completion of these various procedures, I again met with Dr. Hilgers for an hour. We reviewed the videotape of my laparoscopic surgery, and he suggested a hormone treatment to address the problem of low estrogen. He also informed me that I might have a lingering thyroid abnormality, though he added that it was a not-well-understood condition and one for which he was offering an experimental treatment. He said he would need further information about my health over a period of another month before deciding whether I qualified for the experimental treatment. I appreciated his candor in explaining that this was not his field of expertise and a not-well-understood condition. At any rate, I never got to try the experimental treatment: within weeks of receiving my treatments in Omaha, and to my utter surprise, I became pregnant.

PREGNANCY

Anyone who has experienced infertility and then become pregnant will know what I mean when I write, "I couldn't believe it." All human history to the contrary, one reaches a point where you don't really believe human coupling results in babies. When I finally got around to taking an early pregnancy test in August 2003, six months after finding out about the Pope Paul VI Institute, and only one month after my treatments, I could not believe my eyes. I had been warned that it may take months for my body to "readjust" and not to expect overnight results. But I got overnight results…after years of time wasted. And I had not realized that the care provided by the Institute continues into pregnancy. Dr. Hilgers is a specialist in miscarriage prevention, and within 24 hours of confirmation of my pregnancy, he recommended progesterone supplements to help ensure a healthy pregnancy. Although I am seeing a local OB/GYN and will deliver this spring in my hometown, the Institute has continued oversight of my progesterone levels and has completed three ultrasounds for me.

SUMMARY

In sum, my fertility-related diagnoses included: endometriosis, partially blocked fallopian tubes, low estrogen prior to ovulation/premature follicle rupture, and possible thyroid complications. NONE of these conditions was detected, or even raised as possibilities, by my other previous doctors.

My treatments at Dr. Hilgers' direction included: laser surgery for endometriosis; treatment to clear out my fallopian tubes; and a prescribed regimen of daily Vitamin B$_6$, daily prenatal vitamins (of course), Clomid on days 3-5 of my cycle, and an antibiotic on days 11-15 of my cycle.

I don't understand why so many other OB/GYNs take a piece-meal approach to fertility evaluation, especially in women older than 30. I also don't understand, apart from the question of morality, why so many OB/GYNs are so quick to push artificial reproductive technology. This technology seems to be promoted sometimes, if not often, in the absence of a full initial reproductive evaluation. There seems to be a mindset today to go "high-tech," without re-gard for the fact that this may be just layering a "solution" on top of undiagnosed problems, and without regard for the fact that other solutions are much easier and less costly for the couples involved.

For all of the above reasons, I am now encouraging friends and friends of friends who experience infertility to contact the Pope Paul VI Institute. Certainly for Catholic couples, it is a bastion of hope and reaffirmation. And from a secular point-of-view, it is still prob-ably the best reproductive care available for most health problems (and the most thorough, at least, for receiving a diagnosis). As my non-Catholic brother proclaimed to my non-Catholic family when I announced my pregnancy, "those Catholics sure know how to do babies!"

Editor's Note: Olivia June Colloton was born on April 21, 2004 weighing 6 lbs. 12 oz. Mom says, "She is just a dream!"

NaProTECHNOLOGY Treats Problems Not Just Symptoms
Amy Schenk

I began seeing Dr. Hilgers at the Pope Paul VI Institute in December of 1992. I was a newlywed and my husband Pat and I had just moved to Omaha from Lincoln the summer before. I initially started out with the Institute, not necessarily knowing that I would have infertility issues, but because I was looking for a doctor who was pro-life and performed no abortions. I had heard of Dr. Hilgers when I was learning how to chart with the **CREIGHTON MODEL Fertility***Care*™ **System**. Before my first appointment, I was sent a questionnaire asking me specific questions about my cycle, my state of mind at certain times of the month, and other health questions. I was surprised at how well this doctor already knew me before I even walked into his office. I was having problems with my moods and really felt at certain times of the month that I was losing my mind. Little did I know that I had PMS and that Dr. Hilgers was going to help me as much as he has.

At my first appointment, Dr. Hilgers said in so many words that he was pretty sure I had a hormone deficiency and could possibly have problems conceiving. I was worried and scared, as I had always wanted children. I was from a large family and an elementary teacher. I just could not picture my life without children.

Having said that, as concerned as I was, I had a sense that if something was wrong, I was with the right person. Even though I had just met this man, I had faith that if there was a solution, this was the person to find it. In conjunction with the information from my **CREIGHTON MODEL** chart, Dr. Hilgers ordered a series of blood draws at specific times in my cycle. Once completed, Dr. Hilgers confirmed that I had Premenstrual Syndrome (PMS) and ordered progesterone injections on certain days after I ovulated as well as a few other medications to alleviate the symptoms I was having. This alone was a huge relief to both my husband and me. I have no doubt that if left untreated, this alone could have caused some problems in my marriage.

I had hoped that treating the hormone deficiency would address any infertility problems that I had. After about a year, I became concerned when I still had not conceived. My husband and I often had to remind ourselves of our faith in Dr. Hilgers and his staff. An ultrasound series was ordered and it was discovered that my eggs didn't fully mature. Another piece of the puzzle fell into place.

Sometime after that, Dr. Hilgers performed a laparoscopic procedure. Endometriosis was discovered as well as a blockage in my tubes. The endometriosis was taken care of during the procedure, but my tubes were unblocked a short time later. Interestingly, this simple procedure was not covered by my insurance even though I had infertility coverage. They said they would have covered the more invasive, more expensive procedure of an abdominal surgery with six to eight weeks' recovery. With the procedure I had, I was back at work the next day. Now I had the stress of taking them to court. Almost two years later I won and they paid.

I include this part of my story for two reasons. First, you can fight the insurance company and win. Second, this illustrates Dr. Hilgers's commitment to women in treating the problem and not just the symptoms and how many insurance companies often hold it against him and his patients.

After having my tubes unblocked, Dr. Hilgers started me on a low dose of Clomid in addition to the progesterone. I was discouraged after the first month when I wasn't pregnant. I had resigned myself to a life without children. I thought that if it were going to work it would have worked in the first month. I went ahead and tried again for a second month. Seven days after my Peak, I had a day of light bleeding. Once again, I was discouraged. We had an appointment a week or so later. I had a blood draw previous to my appointment. At my appointment, Dr. Hilgers came in, took one look at my chart and drew a big plus sign at the end of my chart. We were stunned and pleased to learn we were pregnant! Apparently the light bleeding was implantation bleeding. We felt so blessed and once again assured that we were at the right place.

The pregnancy was not without its difficulty. My progesterone levels were not where they should have been and I was on progesterone injections several times a week. I also started light cramping early in the pregnancy. Ultrasound showed that my cervix had "dimpling," indicating that my cervix was beginning to dilate. I was placed on bed rest for several months while Dr. Hilgers monitored the dilation via ultrasound. Finally at 19 weeks Dr. Hilgers decided to place a cerclage on my cervix to prevent any further dilation. I continued on the progesterone injections and the rest of the pregnancy was relatively uneventful. Finally, a week past my due date, I was induced. After a rough 14 hours of labor and losing the baby's heart rate, an emergency C-section was performed by one of Dr. Hilgers's associates. Our son, Joseph Patrick, was born on October 20, 1994. It was a great day owed mostly to Dr. Hilgers and his staff. We believe that had we been with another doctor and lucky enough to conceive, we probably would have miscarried either due to the low progesterone levels or from my cervix opening too early. Once again, thanks to **NaProTECHNOLOGY**, Dr. Hilgers was treating the problem and not the symptoms.

When Joe was seven months old, we decided to try again. After a few months of trying, we started on Clomid again, and our daughter, Jennifer Marie, was born by cesarean on May 1, 1996. The second pregnancy was much less eventful; however, I was still on progesterone injections and monitored closely for any cervical changes. Thankfully no cerclage was necessary.

We felt so blessed to have two healthy children. We were busy for several years with Joe being 19 months when Jenny was born. Some days were a blur, but we were thankful. We thought our family was complete. I continued seeing Dr. Hilgers for the PMS, hormones, and endometriosis.

Pat and I had talked of trying for another baby but didn't know if we were up for all that we went through to conceive Joe. We were also afraid that the five years since Jenny was born had probably left a window for the problems, such as the blockage in the tubes, to return. We thought maybe we would try in the fall of 2001 to see if we could conceive again, but the most we would do was try Clomid; no surgeries. However, God had other plans, and in June of 2001,

I discovered I was pregnant! This was a shock, as we weren't really trying. I was on a prescription decongestant for an ear infection, and this apparently threw my charting off. I even called Dr. Hilgers's office and told the head nurse, Linda, that I thought I might have an ovarian cyst since I missed my period. I just really didn't think that I could get pregnant without help. I never understood what it was like when other people found out they were pregnant when they didn't expect it or weren't trying.

Jackson Douglas was born by C-section on February 8, 2002. His pregnancy was the easiest (except for the fact that I was five years older and feeling it!) with progesterone shots being all that was needed. He has been such a joy, and our family truly feels complete.

As Pat and I sit and look at our children, we are grateful for Dr. Hilgers and his staff. We know we might not have Joseph, or all of our children, if not for their diligence and commitment to life.

Physician Finds Answers
Without Artificial Means
Teresa Schumacher

I have had menstruation problems for as long as I can remember, age of 13 years old and on. I was placed on birth control pills, by a local doctor, to try and alleviate the severe cramps. Unfortunately, I never had any relief from the severe cramps and the major premenstrual symptoms and just learned how to live with them.

When my husband, Kevin, and I began to try and conceive our first child, we had a difficult time becoming pregnant. I went to my regular OB many times, but she continued to assure me that sometimes it takes over a year or so to get pregnant. After two years of trying to conceive, we were finally pregnant; but the OB was not concerned that it had taken us two years. We were blessed with our wonderful daughter, Elisabeth, who was born on June 5, 1996. She was born 3 ½ weeks early, but she was in perfect health.

In January of 1998, Elisabeth had just turned 18 months old and Kevin and I decided to try and conceive a second child. We tried for numerous months with no luck, so I went to see the OB. Once again, she was not concerned that it was taking so long and simply noted that we were able to get pregnant once so not to worry about it; it would happen again. After 18 months of trying, I once again, went back to the OB and told her very assertively that we were concerned and wanted to find out what was happening. At that time, she placed me on Clomid, to stimulate ovulation. I was only able to be on the fertility drug for approximately six months. After that period of time, she took me off of it, due to the possibility of being at high risk of developing ovarian cancer if I stayed on the medication too long. At that time, she sent us to an infertility specialist.

We met with the infertility specialist in February of 2000 and told the doctor our story. She did several ultrasounds on me and felt confident that I was suffering from endometriosis. She scheduled me for a laparoscope in March of 2000 to determine if that was what I had. After the procedure, she informed Kevin that I did have a mild to moderate case of endometriosis and that she had lasered the majority of it out. She then thanked Kevin with the following comment, "Tell your wife thank you. It's people like her that keep me in business." Why we chose to stay with a doctor that could make such a cruel and hurtful comment is hard to explain. The only explanation is simply that we were so desperate to try and have a second child, and we were willing to put up with this in order to achieve our ultimate goal.

In a follow-up appointment, the infertility doctor assured me that she had gotten the majority of the endometriosis but wanted to make sure, so she placed me on Lupron and Depo Provera. This medication was to place my body into a fake menopause state, stopping menstruation. The theory was if I stop the menstruation then the endometriosis would clear up, allowing us to become pregnant. She first gave me a one-month injection and then one month later followed it up with a three-month injection. These shots were horribly expensive, costing around $2,500.00 total, and we had to pay 30 percent of the shots, because the doctor was not a preferred provider. The effects of the medication were absolutely horrible on my body. I felt like I had developed arthritis in all of my joints. Getting out of bed each morning was miserable; it would take me about an hour before I felt like I could function properly. I also experienced hot flashes, but the worst were the constant migraines that I suffered from. Some were so bad, that I literally had to sleep them off.

After four months of being on the Lupron shots and having no results, we went back in for a follow-up appointment with the doctor. She informed us that it may take an extra two months to get pregnant, so we'd wait and see what would happen. After an additional two months and no results, the doctor informed us of our next options. She felt confident that we would be able to get pregnant through artificial insemination. We both expressed to her that we were concerned about the procedure due to the fact we would not be able to take part in any selective reduction. Once again, she felt very confident that this would not occur and the worst that would probably occur would be twins, maybe triplets. We informed her that we would need to think about this since we were very concerned about the possibility of selective reduction. After numerous conversations, Kevin and I decided that we did not want to do this. I called the nurse to ask her what our other options were, and she told me that this was our best option and that we better make a decision soon, because my "biological clock was ticking and this may be your last chance to get pregnant." I had just turned 32 and I was highly offended by this comment and knew that we were not at the right doctor's office for us.

Thank goodness a new friend had told me about Dr. Hilgers and I called to find out how soon we could be seen. So, after 2 ½ years of trying to conceive and many heartaches and increased feelings of depression, we finally met Dr. Hilgers in November of 2000. Even before meeting Dr. Hilgers, the wonderful receptionists had scheduled us to begin attending the **CREIGHTON MODEL Fertility*Care*™ System** charting method, to learn how to begin to use the method in order to achieve pregnancy.

In meeting with Dr. Hilgers, he stated that he first wanted to do a hormone study to see if I was having any hormonal imbalances. This study was based on my charting cycle and there were approximately 12 blood tests that were performed during my one menstrual cycle. Dr. Hilgers also looked at the previous films from my first laparoscope and could clearly see that she had not gotten all of the endometriosis and that she had lasered barely any of it. He scheduled me for another lap in January of 2001. Through this procedure, he was able to determine that my endometriosis was severe and that he was only able to laser some of it and would need to do a full laparotomy. He had to surgically remove the majority of the endometriosis due to it being attached to my ovaries and my bowels, which he could not laser.

In March of 2001, Dr. Hilgers performed this surgery on me, which is very similar to having a C-section. I stayed in the hospital for five days and had an additional five-week recovery at home. Dr. Hilgers felt very confident that he had gotten the majority of it, but wanted to assure me that the endometriosis was not my only problem, I also suffered from an ovarian dysfunction and a hormonal imbalance. This was the first time in over six years that a doctor could actually tell us what was wrong and not just continue to say that a pregnancy would happen or try to just push all the fancy infertility drugs and procedures. Kevin and I both really respected Dr. Hilgers's honesty and his desire to truly solve the problem. Due to my hormonal imbalance and ovarian dysfunction, Dr. Hilgers placed me on injections of progesterone at certain times during my cycle, based on the charting method. Also, Dr. Hilgers continued to do numerous blood tests and ultrasounds to try to determine why we were not getting pregnant.

In November of 2001, I informed Dr. Hilgers that we were almost done trying. After four years of constant heartbreaks, I knew that I could not do this emotionally anymore. He informed us that he thought that I might be suffering from a thyroid system dysfunction. He explained the disorder and stated that he would have me take a compound, called T3. I would need to take this exactly every 12 hours around-the-clock and would have to monitor my temperature and my pulse four times a day. Kevin and I decided to try the T3 compound, but we had both decided that this would be the last avenue that we would pursue.

Approximately two months after I began taking the T3, I was a few days late starting my period. I did not even contact Dr. Hilgers's office, because I was so tired of having negative pregnancy tests and knew I could not handle one more. However, when I called in my weekly temperature results for the T3 charting on January 3, 2003, Dr. Hilgers's nurse asked me where I was in my cycle. I informed her that I was Peak + 19. She indicated to me that I might be pregnant and that I should come in that day for a pregnancy blood test. I informed her that I was hesitant to do this, due to all the negative results. However, she convinced me to come in for a pregnancy test.

On my way home from work around 3:30 p.m. I stopped and had the blood test. The nurse informed me that they would still try and run the test today but would definitely call me by tomorrow. Both Kevin and I had convinced ourselves not to get our hopes up, due to all the numerous times that we had been so incredibly disappointed. The phone call came in at around 4:30 p.m. that we were definitely pregnant and that I needed to rush back to their office for a progesterone shot. I had been on the T3 for exactly 50 days when we conceived. Dr. Hilgers's nurse, Linda, knew that Dr. Hilgers would be thrilled with our news. He was at the Rose Bowl game in California and Linda called him on his cell phone to tell him the news! He was so excited. I can't even begin to explain in words how excited we were; all I could do was cry tears of joy. Our daughter, who was 5 ½ years old at the time, was beyond excited. She had prayed for a baby brother or sister for many years. All of our prayers were finally being answered and we were the happiest family and definitely felt like the luckiest one at that moment. That night was definitely exciting and very busy!! We had our daughter call all of our family and friends to inform everyone that she was going to be a big sister!!!

During the majority of the pregnancy, I was at Dr. Hilgers's office one to two times a week receiving progesterone shots. I had blood tests done every two weeks in order to determine my progesterone level. Everything was going great and I was feeling good. However, when I reached week 22 of my pregnancy, I began having some contractions. Dr. Hilgers immediately placed me on Brethine, which is a medication to stop the uterus from contracting. I had to take this medication every four hours around-the-clock. The medication worked great and stopped the contractions for approximately three weeks. When I reached week 25, the contractions were beginning again, and I was placed on bed rest for two days, and Dr. Hilgers started me on an antibiotic IV two times a week. The combination of the progesterone shots, the IVs, and the blood tests every two weeks to determine my levels, allowed our baby to stay in and continue to grow. The remainder of the pregnancy was difficult physically, but I was willing to put up with anything in order to receive our small miracle.

Our miracle arrived 3 ½ weeks early. Alexander was born on August 15, 2002 at 8:37 p.m. Alexander was 20 inches long and weighed 6 lb, 10 oz. He was a perfect and healthy baby boy and he was definitely our second miracle from God.

Our little miracle is now 18 months old as I finally take the time to put our story down in writing. As I write this, I recall as if it was yesterday all the pain and disappointment that we went through for so many years trying to conceive a second child. Unless you have personally experienced infertility, you could not even begin to understand the tremendous emotional roller coaster that a person can experience, not to mention the impact that it has on the entire family unit. I can not adequately express the disappointment and sorrow that our daughter experienced for wanting a baby brother or sister so badly and it not happening for six long years. But the majority of my memories focus around the fact that we were finally able to conceive and experience the miracle of the birth of our healthy baby boy.

My words alone do not even begin to truly express how thankful we are for Dr. Hilgers and the entire staff at Pope Paul VI Institute, for everything that they have done for our family. Dr. Hilgers is a very intelligent physician and a researcher who continues to strive to find the answers to help out his patients. Dr. Hilgers is completely different from all of the other infertility physicians in this area, due to the fact that he does find the answers and will assist people in becoming pregnant without utilizing artificial ways. Dr. Hilgers and his staff are truly remarkable people who genuinely care about their patients and their patients' families. We have received outstanding care from them, and I would highly recommend them to anyone who is having difficulty getting pregnant or experiencing a high-risk pregnancy. We will never forget what Dr. Hilgers and his entire staff have done for our family. They will always hold a very special place in our hearts.

A Healthy Baby at Age 45
With Help of **NaProTECHNOLOGY**!
Karen Renzelli

1998! It was a heart-wrenching year for me. My beloved mother died in February after finding out she had cancer in November. In May, my husband, Frank and I discovered the little boy I was carrying had Trisomy 18, Edward's Syndrome, a lethal anomaly. He was stillborn on September 18, 1998 at thirty-seven weeks gestation. I was 41 years old and I felt devastated and hopeless. At this age could I get pregnant again? Could I have a healthy baby? Before my mother died she told me, "You'll have your family." Those words of hope remained in my mind and heart.

I went to a Marian Conference in Pittsburgh, Pennsylvania on November 1, after losing our son, Joel Samuel Renzelli, and I prayed in my heart and asked God to give me another baby. A man came up to me after communion and said the Holy Spirit inspired him to give this card to me. On the card was a picture of St. Gerard, the patron saint of Motherhood. (A friend enrolled me in the St. Gerard Society to receive newsletters and articles about women who pray to have children and can't for some reason. Some do conceive.) I took this man's gesture as a sign from God. I believed God was telling me He heard my prayer, to keep praying and to have hope. That same month my cousin, Elizabeth, conceived a baby at the age of 46. I believed God was showing me it was possible to have a baby. I knew it was possible, though rare, but was it God's will for me?

I wanted to do all I could - according to the Catholic Church - to conceive. I asked a priest if taking fertility drugs was accepted by the Catholic Church and he said there was no stance against fertility drugs. So I took them, but I didn't become pregnant. My 42nd birthday came. I was so depressed I cried all day. My husband, Frank, was very firm with me. He asked me where my faith was. All I could think about was how badly I wanted a baby and how old I was.

Then my 43rd birthday came and went. During this time, a new priest came to our parish, Father Tim Grassi. My husband went to daily Mass and served for him. We became friends with him and went out to dinner together. We told him our story and how much we desired a child. He told us about the FertilityCare Center in Charleston, West Virginia. He invited Nancy Botkin, from the FertilityCare Center, to come to Clarksburg, West Virginia to speak to engaged couples about Natural Family Planning, **NaProTECHNOLOGY** and the **CREIGHTON MODEL Fertility*Care*™ System.** He invited me to meet Nancy and hear what she had to say. I went and I asked a lot of questions about women my age getting pregnant. I wanted to learn more about all she was presenting. My husband and I went to Charleston where we met with Nancy, saw slides explaining **NaProTECHNOLOGY** and the **CREIGHTON MODEL**, and received materials, books, and charts.

I began reading the books and charting my cycle, and after three months of charting, Kelly Saad, a nurse who worked for the FertilityCare Center, sent my chart to Dr. Thomas Hilgers at the Pope Paul VI Institute in Omaha, Nebraska. (We also sent medical records dealing with my past fertility history and pregnancies; I had a miscarriage before I conceived baby Joel.) Dr. Hilgers studied my records and suggested doing a hormone profile. I had my blood drawn every other day for a two week period, had it freeze-dried according to specific instructions from Dr. Hilgers, and sent all at once to the Pope Paul VI Institute. They got hormone levels from my blood noting my progesterone level dropped dramatically on a certain day of my cycle (probably causing a fertilized egg to be unable to implant in the lining of my uterus). Dr. Hilgers suggested I take Profasi (Natural hCG) shots four times during specific days of my cycle. This would help my body naturally produce the progesterone it needed. I began taking the shots in August after my 44th birthday. At this age, I lost faith. I didn't really believe I would get pregnant. I took the shots for three months, telling myself it was to prevent PMS, and after the fourth set of shots, my period was late. I called the nurses at Pope Paul VI Institute and they told me to go get a blood test to see if I was pregnant. Could it be? I was to call the hospital lab for the results at 7:00 PM. The results were positive!! I called Pope Paul VI Institute to tell them this wonderful news! Dr. Hilgers started me on progesterone shots right away.

My doctor in Morgantown, West Virginia didn't want me to take progesterone past the third month, but Dr. Hilgers suggested I monitor my progesterone levels closely and keep supplementing with progesterone shots until they were no longer needed. I followed Dr. Hilgers's advice and remained on progesterone until my seventh month of pregnancy.

I turned 45 years old on Tuesday, July 23, 2002 and Elizabeth Claire Renzelli was born the following Tuesday, July 30th, at 4:01 pm. She was named Elizabeth, after my mother. Elizabeth means consecrated to God and Claire means illustrious, bright and shiny. My hope is that she will be radiant because she is consecrated to God. She weighed 7 lbs and 8 oz and she was 19 inches long. The doctor said she was very healthy and oh so beautiful!

Elizabeth is a miracle, a wonderful gift from God, who came to us through prayer and help from Father Tim Grassi, Nancy Botkin and Kelly Saad from the FertilityCare Center in Charleston. I'm grateful for the wonderful staff of the Pope Paul IV Institute in Omaha, Nebraska, and Dr. Tom Hilgers, who I believe receives wisdom and grace from God to counsel and uplift women in their struggles with infertility. I know Elizabeth would not be here if it weren't for these people.

I came to believe my mother was a prophet when she said, "You'll have your family," or she has friends in very high places. She always could be very persuasive and she loved her babies.

2002! It was a very blessed year! The year of our miracle, Elizabeth Claire Renzelli!

God Has a Plan for Our Family
Christine Arndt

I had always dreamed of becoming a mother. Holding my child in my arms, rocking her to sleep, with that unmistakable scent a baby has, with the wisps of hair on her nearly bald head, and those tiny hands, just thinking about it puts a smile on my face. Being from a large Catholic family, one would think it would be easy to achieve. Unfortunately God had other plans.

After my husband and I were married about a year, we decided it was time to try to have a baby. Eight months went by with no luck. I visited my gynecologist in Lincoln and was told that since I was young (24) we should just keep trying, and if after a year we didn't conceive to come back. In the meanwhile, I developed an ovarian cyst and after several months, two laparoscopies, and a stent to repair a ureter that was cut during one of the two previous surgeries, I decided to try a different doctor. I visited another gynecologist in Lincoln and we tried Clomid for a couple of months. I developed several cysts, lots of pain, and no baby. After another visit with him, he said he really didn't have anywhere to go from there.

Starting to get depressed and anxious about conceiving a baby, I started looking for another doctor. I began researching infertility and the various ways of trying to achieve a pregnancy. It was very depressing to find out that most infertility treatments were not in line with the teaching of the Catholic Church. I wanted to have a family more than anything, but I also wanted to be true to my Catholic faith. This was a very difficult dilemma for both my husband and me. He was not Catholic, but was very supportive and understanding of my faith. At times I felt like I was letting him down by not exploring artificial means of conceiving. Our desire to conceive and lack of success was unbearable. Each month was greeted with renewed despair. My friends and family were having children, and while I was happy for them, it was tearing me up inside. Some would even say,

81

"Why don't you have a baby?" My heart felt like a lead weight in my chest. During my research I had discovered the Pope Paul IV Institute and knew several people that had overcome infertility after going there. After much prayer and deliberation we felt it was time to visit with Dr. Hilgers. We had been preparing for this visit by learning and practicing the **CREIGHTON MODEL Fertility*Care*™ System**.

By the time I first saw Dr. Hilgers we had been already trying to conceive for about 20 months. One thing was immediately apparent, Dr. Hilgers had a plan. A plan of trying to figure out what was preventing us from conceiving. After taking my history and asking several questions, he started to develop our plan.

The first step of the plan consisted of a month of blood draws during various days of my cycle. That month I sent several prayers of thanksgiving to God for giving me veins which allowed blood to be drawn easily. Overall my blood levels were good, but a few categories could be improved, so medicine was started. The second step of the plan was an ultrasound series to determine if I was ovulating. The results were also positive, I was indeed ovulating. So we came to the last step, the laparoscopy. After the problems I had with my first two laparoscopies, neither my husband or I were excited about the prospect of another one, but we were desperate and decided that God had led us down this path and had led us to Dr. Hilgers.

In March of 1992, Dr Hilgers performed my laparoscopy; my third in less than a year. The results were mixed; my tubes were open but there was a lot of scarring from my previous surgeries. There was also endometriosis that had not been removed in the prior two surgeries. Dr. Hilgers removed what he could. He also had found a small flap at the end of one of my fallopian tubes for which he suggested additional surgery to remove this in case it was blocking the eggs from getting to my uterus. The surgery was scheduled for May of 1992.

I waited to set up the surgery until my period arrived. Through the blessings of God, I never did have that surgery. I was several days late so I bought a home pregnancy test. It wasn't clear, I couldn't tell if it was positive or negative (either that or I couldn't believe that it could be positive). I called Dr. Hilgers's office and they suggested a blood test. I will never forget the call back from the nurse telling me that I was pregnant. I started crying immediately and then wasn't sure what to do next. My husband was overjoyed when I shared the news with him; our prayers had been answered. The surgery that Dr. Hilgers had performed had worked our miracle.

My pregnancy was rather uncomplicated. My husband gave me progesterone shots twice a week for the first four months, but otherwise, everything was normal. I continued to travel to Omaha throughout the pregnancy. I couldn't go back to another doctor in Lincoln after all that Dr. Hilgers had done for us. On February 2nd, my daughter was taking her time, so Dr. Hilgers induced me. After a brief labor she was born at 11:30 am, a perfect 7 lbs. 6 oz. We were overjoyed, our dreams had came true, we were finally parents! We were so happy to have a child that we didn't mind any of the trials of becoming new parents. We were thrilled by each new stage, by all the firsts; we just loved being her Mom and Dad.

We never did really try to prevent a pregnancy after she was born. We wanted God to decide when we would have another child. Once again, we didn't think he would take so long.

Two and a half years after our daughter was born, Dr. Hilgers performed, yet another, laparoscopy and found more endometriosis. He removed what he could, and again, I immediately became pregnant. Unfortunately this baby wasn't meant to be, I miscarried in my sixth week of pregnancy. This was a very dark period for me. I couldn't believe that God had taken my baby away from me. Most people didn't understand. I miscarried so early that they thought it was no big deal. They didn't understand, after all the longing to have children, the joy of learning we were pregnant again; it was almost too much to bear. The sadness was so great that I prayed to God that if he was going to have me miscarry again, that I would rather not get pregnant at all. After all those years of longing for our first, I didn't want any more if it carried the pain of losing another one. We were just thankful that God decided to bless us with one child. It wasn't as though we did anything to prevent a pregnancy, but I stopped going to see Dr. Hilgers and we just stopped trying.

After a year, the darkness had lifted and I started longing for another baby. So I started seeing Dr. Hilgers again. I tried various medicines, I went on Lupron to try to help my endometriosis. Most of these had bad side effects with no results. It was hard to know what to do. I would try for several months and then get discouraged and stop everything. Then I would long for another baby and start trying again. This went on for a couple of years.

Finally in the fall of 1997 Dr. Hilgers once again performed a laparoscopy. This one was not as successful as the first. I now had severe endometriosis, it was too severe to remove via a laparoscopy. Dr. Hilgers suggested major surgery to try to remove it. After battling with my insurance company, they finally agreed to pay, so in November of 1998 I had major abdominal surgery to remove my endometriosis. After six weeks we started trying again to conceive. After a few months Dr. Hilgers put me on a very low dose of Clomid, as he had discovered that my body was very sensitive to the medicine and I could only handle a very low dose. Still we had no luck. After much prayer and discussion we decided that I had been through enough; we were done. We had been blessed with a healthy daughter whom we loved more than anything and we were happy with that.

Throughout the previous couple of years, my parents were having major illnesses. My father had a kidney removed followed by a second heart bypass surgery. Then it was discovered that he had bladder cancer. My mother, meanwhile, was having muscular problems and was finding it difficult to walk and move about. They had stood by us, had supported us emotionally, and prayed for us throughout our years of trying to conceive. Now it was time for me to help them. In November of 1999, I was going with them to the Mayo Clinic. This visit was to determine if my dad's heart was strong enough to withstand a surgery to remove his bladder, and while we were there they were going to evaluate my mom and see if they could help her.

A week before we were to leave, I determined that I was a week late in getting my period. Trying not to get my hopes up, I bought a pregnancy test. This time I didn't need a blood test to confirm it; I knew it was true, I was pregnant. I ended up going with them to Mayo, during which time I had to arrange for a nurse to give me my progesterone shots. My father's surgery was scheduled for a couple of weeks later and they determined that my mother's muscular problem was related to her cholesterol medicine. With the excitement of having their twelfth grandchild, they both recovered quickly. God worked several miracles for our family late that year.

Throughout the entire nine months of this pregnancy, I had the progesterone shots. Other than that, everything was normal, except that the baby was breech. On July 1, 2000 our second daughter was delivered by Dr. Hilgers via cesarean section. To this day I truly believe that God granted us our second miracle just when our family needed her the most. She was just the blessing that my parents needed to help them recover. The pregnancy gave them hope for the future and they wanted to be there to welcome her.

Our years of struggling with infertility have brought my husband and I very close to each other. We have discovered that together we can handle whatever God has planned for us. Before the birth of our first daughter, we learned how to communicate our feelings to each other, especially when we were struggling. After the birth of our first daughter we shared the joy of parenthood. We were there for each other for support when we miscarried our second child. The birth of our second child was another time of joy; the growth of our family only enhanced our love for each other. God has truly blessed our marriage and our family.

Dr. Hilgers and the Pope Paul VI clinic have provided us with help in overcoming infertility while respecting my Catholic faith. Without Dr. Hilgers and his clinic I don't know if we would have experienced the joy of being parents and having a family. We are so blessed to have this faith-inspired clinic in Nebraska!

We continue to pray that we will be blessed with yet another child. We know we have been greatly blessed by God, but we still yearn for more children. I recently had my sixth laparoscopy where once again endometriosis was present. I continue to visit Dr. Hilgers and hope that someday I will once again discover that I am pregnant. The odds are against me because I am getting older and have scar tissue from all my surgeries, but we know that God works in mysterious ways and just maybe he has plans of blessing us with another child. Meanwhile we enjoy our two daughters, and everyday we thank God for both of them and for each other. God has a plan for our family; we just have to be patient and see what comes next.

First Find the Problem - Then Fix it
Julie Wynegar

My first introduction to Dr. Hilgers was a year before I was to be married. My parish priest wanted me to learn more about Natural Family Planning. Shortly after my fiancé, Mark, and I began marriage instruction, we consulted with Tamara Weeks, our FertilityCare Practitioner. I felt very confident with her and well prepared to use the **CREIGHTON MODEL FertilityCare™ System** for the purposes of achieving and avoiding pregnancy after we were married.

Mark and I were married in April 1994. As the months passed we were using FertilityCare to achieve a pregnancy. However, this reliable method was not working for us. I had been noticing through my charting that I was having limited-to-dry mucus cycles and short post-Peak phases. It was in the spring of 1996 that I was becoming concerned and a little discouraged.

In March of 1996, Mark and I had our first consult with Dr. Hilgers. The first moment I met him, I knew he was right for us. He was so kind and caring. He agreed with me that even though it had only been two years trying to conceive, this merited further testing. I remember him elaborating to Mark and I what Pope Paul VI Institute is and defining to us what infertility is, and explaining endometriosis. He also explained to us what his methods of treatments are versus the methods used by other infertility doctors. He wanted us to fully understand that artificial insemination was not an option there partly because it is not solving the underlying problem. I believe his words were, "I need to know what the problem is and try to fix that."

The first step in determining treatment was to do a hormone series testing. This was just a series of blood draws that would give my hormone levels. I also had ultrasounds to see if and when I was ovulating. Through my charting and ultrasounds, he was confident that my troubles were caused by endometriosis.

In April 1996, Dr. Hilgers scheduled an outpatient laparoscopy to visually examine and laser off some of the endometrial tissue. Unfortunately, what Dr. Hilgers found was an enormous amount of endometriosis growing outside of the uterus. The extent of the endometrial tissue was everywhere. He found it extensively on the ovaries, bowels and appendix, and also on other organs. The conclusion was that this was too much to correct during this surgery. He later met with us at his office to show his findings. He had a video of the laparoscopy. I was shocked to see the magnitude of the endometriosis findings. We agreed with him, that I would need to undergo major surgery, and we scheduled it for three weeks following the laparoscopy.

The surgery was a lengthy five hours. He met with Mark after the surgery to inform him that it was a successful surgery. Two months after I had the surgery, we resumed trying to achieve a pregnancy with the help of a low dosage of Clomid taken on days 3 through 5 of my cycle. I was also taking Trexan and Amoxicillin to increase the mucus that would enable me to chart better.

In June 1996 I found out I was pregnant! We were so happy. We went to Dr. Hilgers to make sure all was fine. I would go into the office to have my progesterone levels checked. From the beginning of this pregnancy the levels were too low. I was getting progesterone shots to help boost the levels. Unfortunately, this did not improve, and I ended up miscarrying at seven weeks. This was hard to take, mainly because this would have been our first baby.

Time passed and we were trying again to conceive with the use of Clomid. In September 1996 I was back in Dr. Hilgers's office taking another pregnancy test. I was indeed pregnant! I was getting progesterone shots twice a week until about 17 weeks. We had our baby boy July 3, 1997.

Our second successful pregnancy was similar to the first in that I needed to go through the hormone series, checking levels. This time it took one year of being on Clomid, but eventually I became pregnant again. We were ecstatic! Over half of this pregnancy I needed progesterone shots. We had a healthy baby boy June 10, 2000.

Then all of a sudden I got pregnant totally by surprise in January

2001. I hadn't seen Dr. Hilgers, nor had I come to him for infertility issues. However, this pregnancy resulted in a miscarriage early. I was spotting and it wasn't improving with progesterone shots. We were sad to have lost our baby; however, I bounced back easier with this miscarriage, probably due to my other two little miracle babies at home.

Once again, taken by surprise, I got pregnant in March 2001 with no help from Dr. Hilgers. We had yet another baby boy born November 27, 2001.

I am very pleased with the treatment I received at the Pope Paul VI Institute. Through the **CREIGHTON MODEL Fertility***Care*™ **System**, **NaProTECHNOLOGY** and Dr. Hilgers, we learned how to treat the endometriosis and to appreciate the gift of having children. After having gone through the surgeries, I respect and understand what many women endure to be able to have children. I admire Dr. Hilgers for his achievements in infertility and reproductive disorders and especially as a selfless physician in today's society.

Thanks for Educated, Loving Approach to Family Care
Theresa Barron-McKeagney

I met Dr. Hilgers in 2000. We had been trying to have another child since the early 1990s and had been unsuccessful. We attempted different medical procedures and different doctors, but to no avail. Most of the procedures were quite expensive, but we had faith that we would be successful in achieving our goal, to add another member to our family. After about three years of expensive and painful medical procedures, we decided to stop. My sister had told me about the Pope Paul VI Institute at this time. I didn't know anything about the organization nor about Dr. Hilgers. I decided to stop in one afternoon, somewhat ambivalent at this point, discouraged that time was slipping away. It had been a long ten years of trying to have another child. The staff was very affirming and listened to me. We set up an appointment to visit a Practitioner who would go over a method called the **CREIGHTON MODEL FertilityCare™ System** with us. I thought to myself, "Method? What method?"

My husband and I then started on an interesting journey of listening and watching my body signals on a monthly basis. For an already educated person, I found that I knew very little about the monthly routine of a woman's body. An added benefit was that my husband and I spent more time together attempting to reach our goal. Our counselor would sometimes comment that I looked very tired and worn out, which my family had been telling me for years. Others would say that it was just my lifestyle and job, which added a lot of stress to my life. I had known that I felt tired and worn out for years. I'd had my blood checked for signs of thyroid disorders and other things, but all the tests would reveal nothing. So, I just dealt with my tiredness by treading onward; I had no choice. Month after month came and passed with no success in adding to our family.

We continued to see our counselor at the Institute and I was scheduled to visit with Dr. Hilgers. I will always remember meeting him. He's a very encouraging and warm person whom I immediately trusted. After some tests, he stated that I may have endometriosis because of recurrent pains that started in my lower abdomen areas and would shoot down my legs. I had been dealing with these pains for years, but no one had suggested that I needed a laparoscopy to figure it out. At this point, I was so pleased that something could be done, I agreed to the surgery. It was true, I had some endometriosis, and Dr. Hilgers showed me from the surgery film what pain that caused me for years. What seemed like such a common sense diagnosis that may have contributed to my problems with conceiving, was in part, simple. From there Dr. Hilgers proceeded to eliminate other contributing factors that may have been barriers.

Unfortunately, my age at this time didn't help our cause; I was approaching 41. We continued with different treatments. What I appreciated most about Dr. Hilgers's approach was his explanations for what might be occurring with my body. Before, I felt like all the decisions were really being made with my consent of course, but we didn't have a clue as to why these procedures were the best. With Dr. Hilgers I attempted taking medicines to help my reproductive cycle and wore a catheter with a needle inserted in my wrist for two weeks at a time; it hurt, but I endured. Dr. Hilgers was very honest and straightforward when he told us that this may be the last resort. I really felt like I had tried all there was to try and would be at peace with the end result.

In June 2001, Dr. Hilgers did more blood tests and found that what is a natural stimulant that is related to our brains was very low in my body, he prescribed a medicine that uplifted my spirits. I felt like a new woman. That summer he also ran more blood tests because he suspected that I had a deficiency called the human growth hormone deficiency. The symptoms were those that I had lived with most of my life; fatigue, inability to concentrate, unexplained weight gains, dry hair, poor circulation (always cold). When he asked me about my list of symptoms, we went down the list checking off each and every one. Again, I felt like the world was about to break open! This condition that I had lived with for years, could really be cured?

Dr. Hilgers explained that sometimes people took shots for this condition, but it was very expensive. So, he said if my blood tests results indicated this condition existed, he would recommend specific vitamin regimens. I was so thrilled when the results indicated that I had this deficiency! It wasn't all in my head, nor in my work, etc. It was a real organic issue! So, I began taking the vitamins that July 2001. I felt again like the burden had been lifted. I was a new woman, with energy that was unreal. All from vitamins that were 100 percent natural, but replaced something that was missing organically in my body. I lost nearly 50 pounds, and people started commenting how much younger I looked. I had energy and vitality, I could concentrate and I was losing weight. Evidently, the vitamins were supplying my body with nutrients that it couldn't absorb before the vitamins. I've told Dr. Hilgers I will never stop taking these miracle vitamins. We thought this condition could potentially impact my fertility as well, but to no avail.

We then starting thinking about being foster care parents with potential adoption. We were fortunate to have this opportunity and to realize that parenting little ones was beyond our abilities at this point in our lives. Our foster care children are now with wonderful adoptive parents, and we are a critical part of their lives as godparents. I trust that God truly had a plan for our family: my husband, our biological son and me. Dr. Hilgers is truly blest in his abilities to help people reach their goals.

As I said frequently when our foster children were with us, God sends us just what we need, when we need it. Although what is sent may not be what we envisioned praying for, it is what God intends for us. When we believe that His will be done, then we can truly serve in the manner He always desired for us. The path may be very unclear to us, but it is always clear to God. We will always be indebted to Dr. Hilgers for all the assistance he gave us, the forthright answers, the sensible approaches to medical interventions. We only wished we had met him earlier in our lives, but then again, God's will was done. I have recently come into a professional position that is very challenging and rewarding. Our son just turned 21 years old and he is a constant joy and brings us new revelations every day. We thank Dr. Hilgers for taking such an educated and loving approach to caring for our family.

Institute is Doing God's Work
Margaret Bereit

My name is Margaret Bereit and I am writing this account of my experience with Pope Paul VI Institute because I believe so strongly in what they do. I have had first-hand experience with the institute and with Dr. Hilgers, to whom I am forever grateful.

My husband, David, and I had been married for several years and had been trying unsuccessfully to have a baby for three of those years. We had been to several doctors and no one was able to help us or figure out why we weren't able to conceive. At that time, we met Randy McCaslin who was serving as the director of the **Fertility*Care*™ Center of Central Texas, Inc**. He educated us about the **CREIGHTON MODEL Fertility*Care*™ System**, charting, and how we could learn a great deal about a woman's cycle. It was absolutely amazing! We had no idea that this option existed, even though we had already been in a sacramental marriage for about four years at this time.

We began to chart and work with a FertilityCare Practitioner. It was very enlightening. Randy suggested that we chart for about three months after we felt comfortable with the method, and then send those charts to Dr. Hilgers. We followed Randy's instructions, sent off the charts, and waited until he received the written response from Dr. Hilgers. We were told that I would need to have blood work done, and from looking at my charts, Dr. Hilgers felt it was likely that I had polycystic ovaries. It was clear that something was definitely not right.

My blood was drawn in College Station, Texas on several specific days in my cycle, and then I shipped this blood to Dr. Hilgers for his lab to run tests on it. From this, Dr. Hilgers determined some of my hormones were too low which, in turn, made it difficult for me to become pregnant. He felt that this was probably caused by polycystic ovarian disease. At this time he felt that I should have a laparoscopic evaluation. He indicated that the laparoscopy could help confirm his diagnosis, as well as enable him to determine if there was anything else wrong.

This process, of course, was not inexpensive. We discussed this with Randy McCaslin, and he helped us put everything into perspective. Randy told us that the procedure would likely cost us about the equivalent of a new car. We thought about this and asked ourselves which was more important to us: a new car, or the possibility of having a baby? The answer was obvious to us immediately, so we stepped out on faith even though we had no idea if our insurance would help to cover any of our expenses. We set a date for my surgery in Omaha, Nebraska at the beginning of June 1997.

This was our first trip to the Pope Paul VI Institute. Upon arriving, I quickly realized that the Holy Spirit was present at the Institute. I was particularly moved by the chapel. The building itself was larger than I had imagined, and everyone working at the office was extremely caring and compassionate. Dr. Hilgers was amazing. In my brief experience with him, I realized that he is a very spiritual man who is devoted to helping women in a beautiful, life-giving way. I could tell that his work was a true calling for him, which was a refreshing change compared with other medical providers whom I had encountered. I had an ultrasound done at the Institute when I first arrived. Then we got to meet Dr. Hilgers, and I had a pap smear.

Approximately two days later I went to Bergan Mercy Hospital to have my surgery. I was nervous (to say the least). My mom and my husband were both at the hospital with me, which I found very comforting. I also had many people praying for me at home in Texas. I really could sense their prayers, and I certainly would have been more nervous if it wasn't for them. The procedure began very early in the morning, and after I had been prepped for surgery, Dr. Hilgers came by to visit with me. He was kind and gentle – like a devoted father. He gently told me what to expect once I was in the operating room, and he asked how I felt. As I was rolled into the operating room, the first thing I noticed was how frigid it was in that room. I did have warm blankets covering me, and that helped tremendously.

Fortunately, the anesthesia started to work immediately upon administration, and the next thing I knew I was waking up disoriented in a different hospital room. When I tried to sit up in bed, I began to throw up from the anesthesia. The nausea didn't last long, and the nurse that was helping me was fabulous. She was very patient, tender, and understanding.

Since my procedure was done as a day surgery, I was able to leave the hospital at the end of the day to go back to the hotel. After a couple more days, I went back to the Pope Paul VI Institute and had another appointment with Dr. Hilgers. He confirmed that I had polycystic ovaries and explained how that was causing my hormones to be "out of whack." He also explained that he had found endometriosis and was able to remove it with a laser during the laparoscopic procedure. He showed us the video of a portion of my surgery. He said that he thought I would be able to have a baby, but he couldn't guarantee anything. He then told me that if we would be able to achieve a pregnancy, it would take at least six months and possibly up to 18 months. Dr. Hilgers then gave me a prescription for Clomid, a fertility drug. He explained that he was giving me a small dosage of the medication, which made me very glad.

We returned home to College Station, Texas, and I began taking the Clomid. All the while I was telling myself not to get my hopes up because it might be 18 months, or possibly never. We also began contemplating adoption as another option if we were unable to achieve a pregnancy on our own. However, God knew what was best for the Bereits, because exactly one month after my surgery I became pregnant.

We could not believe it! Words could not express our joy and gratitude to God and his helper, Dr. Hilgers. I immediately called the Institute in Omaha to tell them, and the nurse told me that I needed to begin progesterone shots to help maintain the pregnancy, which I did. Thankfully, my progesterone levels went up by themselves and I only ended up needing two progesterone shots. (Praise God!)

I had a very healthy pregnancy, and successfully carried our baby to full term. Our little miracle from heaven, Claire Elise Bereit, was born on April 8, 1998. With the help of Dr. Hilgers, we were subsequently able to have another child, Patrick Michael Bereit, born August 20, 2002. Photos of both children now hang on Dr. Hilgers's

Miracle Baby Wall at the Pope Paul VI Institute.

In closing, I could never say enough about how much we appreciate Dr.Hilgers and his entire staff. They are truly doing God's work. They are helping miracles happen daily, and our family is a living testimony to that.

I Found a Doctor Who Looked at Me as an Individual
Stefanie Dunnington

Of course, I want to get pregnant, but I want to know what's wrong with me first? Disappointed again…I found myself frustrated as I left the doctor's office with my unread charting information in one hand and a prescription for Clomid in the other.

Having tried to conceive a child for about a year, early on I had sensed that something was not going as it should. While confiding this to a friend, she told me about a book that explained how to chart your monthly menstrual cycle using your basal body temperature and cervical fluid in order to determine ovulation, etc. My husband and I also decided to take a NFP class to ensure that we were learning the method correctly. After charting for several months though my doctor did not agree, I thought that my suspicions had been confirmed. So began the search for a doctor who would look at me as an individual, take into account the clues that my body seemed to be providing, and put the pieces together in an effort to facilitate health, not just pregnancy. This desire increased all the more several months later when my first pregnancy ended in miscarriage.

I can't remember which organization it was, but after an afternoon of desperate phone calls, searching for somewhere that I might find some answers to what was going on with my body, the man on the other end of the phone commented that Pope Paul VI Institute sounded like what I wanted - would I like their phone number? That was two years into my journey with infertility and several doctors later. At the time we were living in St. Louis, Missouri. A nurse at Pope Paul VI Institute told me to contact a teacher in my area so that I could learn the **CREIGHTON MODEL Fertility*Care*™ System**. As it turned out, the hospital that I drove past everyday to and from work was where I needed to go. Amazingly, the director of the FertilityCare Department there had worked with Dr. Thomas Hilgers since the early years of his research.

Once I had recorded several months of **CREIGHTON MODEL** charts, both my teacher and I mailed a letter to Dr. Hilgers explaining my situation, to see if he would take my case. By this time we had moved to Seattle, Washington. Within a short time Dr. Hilgers responded, stating that he would take my case. In the letter he recommended that "she have a very thorough hormone profile of her menstrual cycle, an ovarian ultrasound series to determine whether or not she is ovulating and whether or not she has polycystic ovarian disease and then a diagnostic laparoscopy and hysteroscopy with endometrial cultures and a selective hysterosalpingogram. With this in mind, we would be able to determine pretty much what is wrong and then based on that we can tailor make a form of treatment for it."

As my teacher read the letter to me over the phone, I quickly realized that my search had ended. This approach was what I wanted. Six months later, a month-long series of blood work was collected in Seattle and mailed to the lab in Omaha. I then flew to Pope Paul VI Institute for the rest of the evaluation. There I had outpatient surgery (at a local hospital) as well as a series of ovarian ultrasounds. After all the pieces were put together, Dr. Hilgers determined that I had polycystic ovarian disease, a lesion inside one of my ovaries, dysfunctional bleeding and hypothalamic pituitary gonadal dysfunction. He felt that the best plan of treatment would be: surgery, in order to perform an ovarian wedge resection on both ovaries as well as removal and biopsy of the growth inside the left ovary; receive hCG injections on key days in the menstrual cycle; and begin taking a very small daily dose of Naltrexone. So, for my 30th birthday, I was in the hospital recuperating from surgery; not exactly how I had envisioned my life. Thankfully, the surgery went well and the biopsy revealed that the lesion was a dermoid cyst, which had nothing to do with my fertility issues.

After several months spent healing, I began taking Clomid each month along with hCG injections and continued the daily regimen of Naltrexone. Of course, I was convinced that I would immediately become pregnant. But, that was not to be. Six months later, finding myself weary of monthly disappointment, thoroughly depressed and flirting with getting off this stupid roller coaster ride in order to pursue adoption, wouldn't you know it; I conceived. My husband and I had decided that if we were still childless by December 2000, we would put all our financial and emotional energies into building our family through adoption. I gave birth to our first son on November 25, 2000. For most of that pregnancy, Dr. Hilgers monitored my progesterone level and prescribed regular injections of progesterone for the health of the pregnancy.

When my son was about 15 months old, we decided to try again. Steadying ourselves for the long haul, we were shocked that on the very first month of taking Clomid, I became pregnant. So, after months of having my progesterone level monitored and receiving regular injections again, I gave birth to our second son on December 22, 2002.

After both of my children were born, I was on the road to serious postpartum depression but Dr. Hilgers prescribed a series of progesterone injections, which thankfully, brought complete relief of all symptoms. Also, to help relieve PMS symptoms and for my long term health, Dr. Hilgers has recommended that I continue to receive monthly hCG injections since my progesterone level is chronically low.

It should come as no surprise that I think all women struggling with women's health issues, fertility related or not, should learn the **CREIGHTON MODEL FertilityCare™ System** and go to Pope Paul VI Institute for treatment.

Pope Paul VI Institute: An Open Door
Janet R. Fisher

I never dreamed my husband and I would be infertile. We were an active, healthy couple and decided to start a family two years into our happy marriage. It should be easy, we thought. My husband, Abe, was 30 and I was 28. We lived on a farm in Northwest Kansas, a great place to raise a family. Our families were close and we were looking forward to making many memories with our children in the years ahead of us. But after a year, we had not created a new life, so we sought help from our family doctor.

After very basic tests, Abe was referred to several urologists. His sperm lacked motility and with further testing, he had varicocele repair surgery. I was referred to an OB/GYN and had numerous tests and a hysterosalpingogram that checked for any problems inside the fallopian tubes and uterus. Both tubes were open and everything appeared fine. The experience was all so surreal—the exams, lab work, surgery, paperwork, charting basal body temperature, and ovulation predictor kits to name a few things.

During this process, we found it very difficult to discuss our infertility with others. The disease was very silent, yet very painful and emotionally draining. We endured many comments from others like, "So, when are you going to have kids?" or "Don't you want to have a family?" "Yes!" I would scream inside of my head, but knew I could never tell them the whole story. It was too complicated and personal. Many times I would daydream of a beautiful baby, curled up on my shoulder fast asleep. I could almost feel the baby's soft breath on my neck and the sweat on its little head! Oh, how I longed to be a mommy! It ached to be around friends with babies and small children to the point that I avoided them. I felt that I didn't belong to those groups because I wasn't a mother.

During those dark times, Abe and I relied on our faith and each other for strength. Strangely enough, there were many blessings that came from our infertility, especially our love for each other. Our relationship grew stronger after hitting rough waters. We always had a strong Catholic faith and it, too, became more solid; our rock and foundation. As time ticked away, it became apparent that our traditional Catholic values would help us set our limits against using certain kinds of assisted technology to achieve a pregnancy. We had decided our purpose in seeking medical help was to make our bodies healthier, so that we would be able to conceive a child through regular marital relations—the way God designed it.

I will never forget one particular scene; it will be burned in my memory forever. Abe and I sat in the office of a very prominent fertility specialist in Denver. We were told that with Abe's sperm, our chances of conceiving the natural way were exceptionally slim. We had just learned his body was producing anti-sperm antibodies. In so many words, we were told "But don't worry, we can make you a baby through in vitro fertilization." We were quick to tell the doctor we were not interested because it was against our Catholic beliefs and inquired about other treatment options. The doctor could not believe what he was hearing from us and after a short time trying to sway our opinion, he shook his head and bid us goodbye.

We were extremely disappointed and discouraged and prayed even harder. A year and a half later, we were given the name of Dr. Thomas Hilgers at Pope Paul VI Institute in Omaha by our best friend. He had received pro-life literature about the medical facility in the mail and passed it on to us. We immediately felt our prayers had been answered! Finally, a pro-life, pro-Catholic medical center that understood us! We read all we could on the **CREIGHTON MODEL FertilityCare™ System** and after four months of instruction on charting my menstrual cycles, we were able to determine my most fertile days (around Peak Day).By charting my cervical mucus and recording information about my periods, I was giving Dr. Hilgers data that would be useful in diagnosis of my infertility.

He felt it was necessary to do a complete hormone study after reviewing my menstrual cycle charts. It meant driving 44 miles round trip daily to the nearest hospital to have blood drawn for several days during each menstrual cycle. We did this for three cycles.

The information proved to be extremely helpful and we began

treatment right away. Abe gave me progesterone shots (It wasn't hard for him to do as he had given cattle shots many times before), and I also took other medications to balance my hormone levels. The entire process made me wonder why other doctors didn't check my hormones to this extent.

It became clear to me that **NaProTECHNOLOGY** and the Fertility-Care System was on the cutting edge and was about getting to the heart of the problem and solving it—finding the source of the disease and curing it. Their vision was to cure the disease through technology; assisting, but not interfering with the natural process of conception. Wow! How powerful! If only more couples were aware of **NaProTECHNOLOGY**! In our past experience many specialists, as competent as they were, were unconcerned about curing our disease, but only with the end results leading, or should I say pushing us toward "making a baby" in a test tube.

During this time, we were reaching the five-year mark of our infertility. I was almost 33 and felt that our time was getting away from us. We began to entertain the idea of adoption. Our best friends had a daughter through an open adoption and it was a very positive experience for them. After investigating the process, our fears were lessened, and after much prayer, we contacted Catholic Charities. We had all the paperwork completed and were included in the "pool" of other prospective parents. We were told that a usual time frame for an adoption was about two years. Our prayer was that God would open doors He wanted us to enter and doors would closed to those paths that were not of His plan. It was out of our hands; we were not in charge. We would remain open to both realms: conceiving a biological child or adoption.

All of our contact with Dr. Hilgers to this point had been through telephone consultations. But after completing the hormone study, we traveled to Omaha to the Pope Paul VI Institute and were in town for 12 days. Immediately upon entering the building, we noticed the chapel in which Mass was celebrated each week. It was comforting to be in a place where Christ was welcomed and obviously present. We met the excellent staff and nurses. The first nurse that gave us care had, just a few months earlier, been through the same tests I was scheduled to have. She told me exactly what to expect and made sure we had all our questions answered before leaving. Dr. Hilgers was extremely professional, knowledgeable, and yet very gentle and compassionate. I felt very comfortable with him right away.

The next day, I was scheduled for laparoscopic exploratory surgery. It was to view the abdomen, outer uterus, fallopian tubes, ovaries, etc. Dr. Hilgers also performed another hysterosalpingogram to check for blockages in the fallopian tubes. Later on that week, we were amazed at the 3-D imaging that was performed each day on my ovaries to view the ovulation process for abnormalities. Thus the reason for a "vacation" in Omaha, since we lived 5 ½ hours away. (There's really a lot to do in Omaha!) The overall findings were surprising. Dr. Hilgers lasered away several areas of endometriosis and also found that my right fallopian tube, which had been open four years ago, was blocked shut. He tried to open it internally, but was unsuccessful. It would take a tedious surgery, with much more recovery time, to cut out the blockage and reconnect it.

It was now up to us to decide if and when we wanted to do the surgery. I immediately felt we had the closure we needed. We had the entire picture and game plan in front of us but still felt it could take many months to achieve a pregnancy. We had both female and male infertility factors to overcome. Summer was just beginning, the busiest time of year on the farm, and I knew I could not afford to be laid up from an additional surgery. So we went home and prayed for more guidance. Abe and I both knew in our hearts that the time spent at the Pope Paul VI Institute had been very successful and was a door we were meant to enter. We had a diagnosis and solutions to cure our disease. We needed to find competent, caring, pro-life doctors that shared our beliefs, and we did!

Four months later, on September 18th, our social worker from Catholic Charities called to tell us a birthmother had chosen us to adopt her baby that was due October 31st. We had been on an emotional roller coaster for the last five years, but were not prepared for this news so soon! After all, we were only in the "pool" for six months. We were shocked, excited, scared, and felt extremely unprepared to become parents at the ages of 33 and 35— those emotions that all first-time parents feel. Most parents have nine months to prepare, but we had maybe six weeks! After adjusting our focus and making a few shopping trips for baby supplies, we were so ready to take on the awesome responsibilities of mother and father.

Our son, Caleb, was born November 8th: a healthy beautiful baby. We took him home with us two days later. And to think, while we were going through our hormone testing and care at Pope Paul VI Institute, our son had been conceived and was being prepared for us. God had this baby planned for us all along!

Now, as new parents, we were too tired to even imagine trying to conceive a child! Our thoughts of resuming treatment for infertility were put on the back burner. Then God gave us another precious son through adoption: Connor, born November 1st the following year, just a week shy of his brother's first birthday. We felt complete, happy, extremely blessed, and. . . . exhausted!

Our story has had many unexpected twists and turns, but is not over by any means. We have not conceived a child yet, but we have not completely given up hope for more babies. We could at any time, resume treatment or adopt additional children. Some people may question whether or not we were really healed. But I can tell you with all my heart, "YES we were." There are many kinds of healings, some physical, emotional, or spiritual. Our time at the Pope Paul VI Institute, now almost four years ago, resulted in all three. We were given excellent medical care as well as love, respect, and hope in a pro-life, Christian environment. What more could we have needed? Dr. Hilgers and his staff are wonderful, caring people and what they are doing for women and couples trying to conceive is amazing! The statistics prove it. Pope Paul VI Institute was a vision of Dr. Hilgers after reading the encyclical, Humanae Vitae, by Pope Paul VI. It is obvious to Abe and I that the hand of God is present there and is continuing to bless their efforts.

By placing our trust in God, we were led down what seemed like a long and weary path at the time; but looking back, it was one that was filled with many blessings! We don't know what doors will open or close on our continued journey, but we know that we were made stronger by our infertility, an unexpected blessing.

Charting Gives Sense of Empowerment
Kendle Haegelin

My name is Kendle Haegelin; I am 26, married with two children. My husband, Chad, and I have been married three years and have been charting the **CREIGHTON MODEL Fertility*Care*™ System** for about two-and-half-years.

I suffered from severe cramps, PMS and heavy periods and had endometriosis. I feel like I have a very complicated gynecological history and had been misdiagnosed for years. My husband and I were very anxious to get help and relief of my problems and treat them using **NaProTECHNOLOGY.**

I started my first menses at the age of 13. From the beginning, I had terrible cramps, diarrhea, headaches, mood swings and weight gains and losses in excess of 30 pounds. I tried diets and exercise and used a heating pad to ease the pain. After high school while attending college, I continued to have these same symptoms but also experienced chronic urinary tract infections and depression. I tried the birth control pill for a short time, but it caused numbness in my legs and weight gain. Over five long years, I was incorrectly diagnosed as having pelvic inflammatory disease, spasmodic bowel, chronic back pain, Girardeau, kidney stones and thyroid problems.

My symptoms worsened in the summer of 2000. I began experiencing severe abdominal pain in July. From July through October, I was given antibiotics, pain killers, and the pill. Finally, the physician found a pelvic mass and scheduled me for surgery. During the surgery, a mass was removed from the fallopian tube and endometriosis that had been discovered was removed by laser surgery.

Chad and I then moved from Houston to Wichita Falls. In January 2001, I again experienced severe back and abdominal pain and, during several visits to the emergency room, was diagnosed with pelvic inflammatory disease. I was given antibiotics and pain killers. I was suffering from severe menstrual cramps, bloating, fibrocystic breasts, weight gain, depression, anxiety and insomnia. My new local physician wanted me to take Lupron or Depo-Provera to prevent the endometriosis from reoccurring. After researching and careful consideration of this request, we decided to seek help from the Pope Paul VI Institute and Dr. Thomas Hilgers.

The summer of 2001, Chad and I attended FertilityCare training in Austin, Texas and began charting with a FertilityCare Practitioner. After three cycles, we wrote to Dr. Hilgers and began the treatment process. I continued to chart and began a hormone profile. In August, we traveled to Omaha, Nebraska for an appointment and surgery with Dr. Hilgers. He performed a laparoscopy, uterine suspension, laser endometriosis and correctly diagnosed me with hypothyroidism and polycystic ovaries and partially clogged fallopian tubes.

After the surgery, my husband and I continued to chart, while taking various hormones prescribed by Dr. Hilgers. The hormone treatment was for the symptoms of polycystic ovaries. Each month we would call in to his office and conduct a chart review with his nursing staff, so that adjustments could be made. During that time period, before the conception of our first child, I had never felt better or more normal. Practically all my symptoms went away; my periods came and went with no cramping or bloating. It was truly a blessing to be in control of my own body, and it was also a relief that I did not have to take the pill or some other drug to get better. Since the surgery, my husband and I have continued to chart and follow my health with Dr. Hilgers. We have conceived two children, carefully planned. Since the birth of my second child, I am beginning to chart again.

In conclusion, charting with **CREIGHTON MODEL Fertility*Care*™ System** has given me a sense of empowerment. I can tell what my body is doing and when I expect menses to occur. I also have experienced relief from PMS, cramps and many other horrible symptoms. The charting method is easy and applicable in many ways to my health. By applying the methods researched by Dr. Hilgers and the Pope Paul VI Institute, I have experienced relief and a sense of control of my body for the very first time.

I've Come to Accept My Body as Unique
Maryann Henrichs

My name is Maryann Henrichs. I'd have to say that my treatment of premenstrual syndrome began in 1994 when I met with Dr. Thomas Hilgers for the first time. My husband and I were trying desperately to have a baby. The obvious problem I had was very long menstrual cycles – 60 days sometimes. I had been on birth control for quite a few years. I'm not saying that was the cause of my long cycles or my infertility, but in my opinion, with everything I know now, it did not help. As part of my treatment, my gynocologist would administer shots of progesterone to get my period to start. We tried many things, but my cycles didn't change, and I wasn't getting pregnant. Little did I know the process would take much patience and work, so what seemed to be desperation at this point was only the beginning. I had no idea how messed up my body really was.

Dr. Hilgers began with a physical and a series of hormone tests. We needed to find out what was causing the long menstrual cycles in order to deal with my infertility. The results showed I had poly-cystic ovarian disease. This was a mouthful – and the word disease is always frightening. He suggested doing an ovarian wedge resection. This was a surgical procedure requiring six weeks recovering time. I had the surgery, and over time my cycles returned to a more normal schedule – normal for me became 33 to 38 days. What a change. I actually knew when one cycle ended and when a new one began. We could now start trying for that baby we so desperately wanted, not realizing there were more issues to address, two being low estrogen and progesterone levels – very key issues for a healthy pregnancy. What I didn't realize at this point, though was how important these levels were to my overall health, pregnant or not.

The **CREIGHTON MODEL FertilityCare™ System** helped immensely, not only to indicate the days of ovulation for the pregnancy aspect, but also so I could see what was going on at the end of each cycle in regard to premenstrual syndrome. When I started charting, I had a hard time determining the days of ovulation because I had very little mucus. Dr. Hilgers suggested taking a sustained release of 500 mg Vitamin B6. This did aid in the detection of ovulation. I found it also lessened the irritability I was feeling the last week of my cycle. I also discovered that sometimes I had days of "brown bleeding" during the last week of my cycle. It would usually begin nine days after the Peak Day and continue until the new cycle began. Dr. Hilgers told me this is one of the symptoms of low progesterone.

It was during the time I was on infertility drugs to get pregnant that I noticed my cycles were more normal. The infertility drugs increased my estrogen and progesterone levels to a more normal level. Therefore, ovulation seemed to be at the same time every month, and I didn't have all the brown spotting at the end of the month. With the exception of the roller coaster ride of emotion that infertility treatment tends to be, I felt pretty good. To insure everything was in order for me to get pregnant, I also had a procedure done that unblocked my right tube. In February of 1998 our prayers and many efforts paid off – I got pregnant, and on November 14, 1998 my son was born. I felt as if the biggest rock had been lifted off my shoulders, and I was closing the door on my infertility and hormone issues. I guess I thought a full term pregnancy would fix everything. After all I not only achieved getting pregnant, but a healthy baby as well. Didn't this mean I was now normal?

After the birth of my son I really didn't think about abnormal hormone levels. My husband and I decided we weren't going to go through more infertility treatments. We were going to enjoy fully the gift God had given us, and if we were fortunate to have another one, that would be great. Again, I really did think my hormone levels would remain normal.

This is when I first experienced, or maybe first really noticed the symptoms of premenstrual syndrome. It was the year my son turned two I noticed I started feeling "different" the last week of my cycle. It seemed to really get worse when winter started. Because I was a stay-at-home mom, I wrote that feeling off to the fact that we had been stuck in the house due to the very cold temperatures and snowy winter. Also, the sun hadn't been shining much. I am one who needs the sunshine in the winter. After my son was born, I quit taking the 500 mg Vitamin B_6 I was taking, but I did continue to take my prenatal vitamins. I felt really irritable and more sad than normal. I felt like I wanted to cry and just scream all at the same time, almost like there was an explosion going on inside my body. Why should I be so sad? I got to be home with my son, my husband had a good job so financially we could still enjoy spending some money on certain things we wanted or an occasional night out with friends, we had a small, but nice home, and we had the good fortune of health in our families. I felt jittery, too. Sometimes my energy level just felt "zapped" and it took everything I had sometimes to do things other than taking care of my son, because I felt so consumed by all these feelings. I don't know if it was more mental exhaustion than physical. I also noticed that the "brown bleeding" at the end of my cycle started up again.

After discussing all this with Dr. Hilgers, he did the blood workup to test my progesterone and estrogen levels on my P+7 day. The tests came back with once again low progesterone and estrogen levels. Dr. Hilgers suggested a maintenance program of monthly hCG (Human Chorionic Gonadotrophin) injections on P+3, P+5, P+7, and P+9 days of my cycle. At first I was very hesitant because the thought of shots again did not thrill me. I swore I was done with shots, blood work, and infertility. As silly as it sounds too, I thought about the monthly expense. My insurance did not cover anything like this. I didn't know if we could afford this every month. Maybe I could just live with the way I was feeling and it would eventually go away. Once again, as with infertility treatments, I felt like I would be controlled every month by the charting, the shots, etc.

In my conversation with Dr. Hilgers, he explained to me how normal levels of progesterone and estrogen are so important for my body and what is supposed to take place every month; so no, this was not something that was just going to go away. He also explained to me what the long term effects could be if my levels remained as low as they were. All of a sudden the expense worry disappeared. My husband, too, assured me how important my physical and emotional health was.

Since 2001 I have been doing the monthly injections of hCG on P+3, P+5, P+7 and P+9 days of my cycle as instructed. My husband administers the shots to me on the specified days every month. I also started taking my sustained 500 mg of Vitamin B$_6$ again. What a difference! I still may feel irritable, but it's not like that uncontrollable irritability I had been feeling, and it's only for a day, not the entire week. I don't feel that incredible sadness I felt. I feel in control. I remember getting together with some girlfriends in December of 2002 and telling them how great I felt, physically and emotionally. Today in 2004 I still feel great. Premenstrual syndrome doesn't haunt my life anymore.

In the beginning, it was all about my infertility and getting that baby we so desperately wanted. I never thought when all this started I'd still be charting my cycle every month. I never would have guessed my husband would be giving me injections of hCG every month. My treatment of premenstrual syndrome has become as regular as eating, drinking, and exercising to others. I've finally come to realize I can't control my low hormone levels, but I can take control of how they affect me every month. I've come to accept my body as unique. I just have to work a little harder to feel and be healthy. It is so worth it. I think we all have issues, it's how we handle and address them that makes us succeed or fail. With the help of God, Dr. Hilgers, my husband, my family, and friends, I have succeeded. I'm so grateful I met with Dr. Hilgers that day back in 1994. He was determined to find out what was wrong, not just give me the quick fix. I am healed!

Tubal Reversal Results in Miracle
Holliey Lambert

I started suffering from endometriosis and severe hormone imbalances when I was 14 years old. Throughout the years I was in and out of various doctors' offices and hospitals, always with the same diagnosis, pelvic inflammatory disease (PID). I began to feel this was the diagnosis doctors would give when they couldn't find the real problem. For years the only way to function was with the aid of pain pills the doctors would prescribe.

After going from doctor to doctor in my search for help, I found a gynecologist who thought some exploratory surgery would give us a better idea of what was wrong. After the surgery, the doctor informed me that I was suffering from a disease called endometriosis and there was no easy cure.

Over the next few years several procedures were performed involving laser treatments and cauterization to remove the deposits of endometriosis. After each of these seven procedures, the pain would subside for 6 to 12 months. It seemed that every time the pain came back it was worse than the time before, and eventually simple things, like getting out of bed, turned into difficult tasks. Amazingly, through all this trouble, I was able to give birth to two beautiful, healthy children, Nathan and Korrissa. Following each pregnancy the pain severely escalated, so after the birth of the second child, during the seventh laparoscopy, it was decided that a tubal ligation, i.e. "tying the tubes," would be a good idea. I was given the impression that this was a simple procedure that could easily be reversed if any more children were wanted in the future and was not informed of the serious ramifications this would have.

A few years later, I met the most wonderful man who is now my husband and the father to Nathan and Korrissa. For several years he stood by and watched me in pain, and we both felt the frustration of not having a cure in sight. When the doctor wanted to schedule another procedure, he felt it was time to find another doctor who could provide a solution. With this in mind he took it upon himself to do some research, and, with the help of the church, he found our angel, Dr, Hilgers.

Living in Colorado, we knew it would not be cheap to see a doctor in Omaha, Nebraska, but with the help of our families and my husband's determination to have me see the best doctor, we were able to make it possible. When we arrived in Omaha our hopes were high but we had no idea what I was about to experience. Dr. Hilgers decided that a laparotomy was in order to remove all the damaged tissue, endometriosis and reverse the tubal ligation.

The surgery was a long procedure, and following the surgery was a long recovery and several series of blood tests, injections and pills. During recovery from the surgery, Dr. Hilgers informed us that he was not given much to work with for the tubal ligation reversal and one of the tubes had a 25 percent chance of functioning. During the recovery and follow-up testing, Dr. Hilgers determined my hormone levels and thyroid levels were not where they needed to be. With all of this information, having another child seemed like an impossible dream.

About a year after the surgery, I began experiencing pain and swelling. Dr. Hilgers continued adjusting the hormone levels and thyroid medication in an effort to provide some comfort. He also helped me with charting my cycle in an effort to conceive another child. Efforts were made for conception for about a year with no success. With the frustration of the pain, the pills, the injections and the inability to conceive a child, it was decided that another procedure was needed to remove any adhesions and possibly the uterus. With the surgery scheduled, it seemed that another child really would be just a dream. To come to this realization at only 27 years old was devastating and heartbreaking.

In February of 2003, the scheduled time for the surgery was upon us and Dr. Hilgers's nurses recommended I take a pregnancy test, just in case. I was expecting the usual heartbreaking negative results when I received a call, "You're pregnant!" My husband and

I could not believe it, I think he is still in shock. All of our prayers were answered just when I'd given up.

Nine months later, after working closely with a local doctor and Dr. Hilgers to help the trouble-riddled pregnancy, I had my miracle, Noah Ryan Lambert. Although I still suffer from pain and have not yet reached resolution of the endometriosis, I thank God every day for the prayers he answered when he brought me, my children, my husband and Dr. Hilgers together.

We Have a Sense of Joyful Contentment with God's Will
Eileen Lyon

It was in May 1989 in a British National Health Service hospital that I first learned that I had endometriosis. I had been admitted to the hospital with severe pelvic pain. An ultrasound revealed very large cysts on both ovaries and the doctor recommended surgery to remove them as soon as an operating theater became available. This was a busy place. Our consultation lasted less than five minutes. The following morning another doctor came to deliver a report of the operation during the usual morning ward rounds. I was greatly relieved when he told me that both ovaries were saved but my joy ebbed as he began to describe how what had begun as a fairly simple laparoscopic procedure had turned into a major operation to remove extensive endometriosis and adhesions (described as stage IV).

I had never heard of endometriosis or suspected I had any gynaeco-logical problems. I accepted the pain I felt each month as normal. My mother complained of similar problems and I had never asked a doctor about it. Indeed, this operation was my first encounter with a gynaecologist. As the doctor outlined the prognosis, he indicated that endometriosis was one of the principal causes of infertility and it was unfortunate that I had such an extensive case at a young age. He also asserted that many patients required a hysterectomy in time. Indeed, he had just done a hysterectomy on another patient a few beds down from me. Again, our consultation lasted less than five minutes. So many questions were just forming in my mind as he went on to the next bed.

In the strange sense of community that develops in these British hospital wards where 25 or so people find themselves thrust together with little privacy, I met the lady who had just had the hysterectomy for her endometriosis. She was feeling very positive about her surgery.

She was 26 and had already had several previous surgeries and extensive hormonal therapy to treat her endometriosis. She and her husband did not wish to have any children, so she welcomed the hysterectomy as the means to end what she called "A chronic and debilitating pain." I remember returning to my bed and feeling absolutely shattered. Was this to be my future: debilitating pain, hysterectomy and no children? At age 23, I had not yet given any thought to my fertility beyond the assumption that someday I would marry and have children. This vision of my future still felt rather distant as I had not yet been on more than a few dates. Yet, all of a sudden, it became very present and important to me.

Before I was admitted to the hospital, I had been awaiting news of my application to Cambridge University to study for a Ph.D. in History. (I had been in Birmingham, England for two years as a Fulbright Scholar and had just completed a Master's degree.) A friend came to visit me in the hospital, bearing flowers and a letter, which indicated not only that I had been admitted to Cambridge but that I would be offered a full scholarship. In other circumstances, this probably would have been one of the most exciting moments of my life, but, at this moment, it seemed like too dramatic an example of one door closing and another opening. I remained somewhat focused on the door that appeared to have closed for me. I spent a couple of months back with my family in Connecticut, recuperating from the surgery and making preparations to go to Cambridge. My parents worked very hard at trying to cheer me up and get me to focus on the opportunities that lay ahead at Cambridge. They had each earned a Ph.D. in Chemistry and spoke of the happiness and intellectual fulfillment that they found in their professional lives. Yet, these words failed to provide me with much comfort, as I could see and had experienced the degree to which love and commitment to their children was at the center of their lives.

I tried to push the endometriosis diagnosis to the back of my mind as I started at Cambridge that fall. This proved to be quite difficult as I continued to have a lot of pain. By February, it was clear that I needed further surgery to separate adhesions from my earlier operation. However, the good news was that this surgery revealed no sign of endometriosis. This really helped me to look forward with hope and excitement about all that might lie ahead. The opportunity to study at Cambridge was a wonderful gift. My life was forever changed on many levels: intellectually, spiritually, and emotionally. In a sense, I really came into my own there, with a clear understanding of my aspirations for the future. I met my future husband during our first week in Cambridge. He had come from South Africa to study for a Ph.D. In Philosophy. We shared a wonderful friendship born of great intellectual chemistry and shared religious beliefs that eventually blossomed into romance.

Our romance seemed to begin just as we were to face a significant practical obstacle. We had completed our Ph.D.s and entered the intensely competitive marketplace for university teaching posts. Gordon found a position at Rhodes University in Grahamstown, South Africa and I at Florida State University in Tallahassee. We left England to take up our new jobs. Much was left unsaid as we parted.

We remained in close contact via e-mail. It was clear as the months went on that we had found in each other a life partner, but a little less clear how to arrange a life together on the same continent. Within a year, I was back in England on research leave from Florida State and so decided to make a short visit to South Africa in December 1995: a trip during which we became engaged and determined to settle in the United States after our wedding. The specter of the endometriosis diagnosis haunted me as I contemplated my marriage to Gordon. We had talked about this very early on in our relationship. Despite the security I felt in our love for each other and Gordon's reassurance that he wished for a life with me, with or without children, I continued to fear that there would be a quiet sadness if we were unable to have children. It would take us another 18 months to sort out the logistical problems of a life together on the same continent. We were married back in Cambridge in July 1997 and settled in Tallahassee in time for the new academic year.

In my first few years in Tallahassee, I did not get established with a primary care physician. Indeed, I felt more confident seeing my British doctor for routine things and was healthy enough and in England frequently enough that this was feasible. This period of my life was coming to an end and the time had come to find an American doctor. I sought recommendations from several individuals I knew in the medical community, which led us to Dr. H. Whit Oliver. He practiced family medicine with obstetrics. We were told that he was a really excellent doctor and a very nice man. No one had told us that he was an NFP-only physician. I made an appointment to see him and braced myself for what I thought would be some level of confrontation over our decision not to use artificial contraception.

A gynaecologist I had seen in Tallahassee a few months earlier had been very hostile to natural family planning and fiercely insistent that oral contraceptives were imperative for treating my endometriosis. None of the doctors whom I particularly respected in Cambridge shared the views. Several of these were leading researchers as well as clinicians. Indeed, one had mentioned in passing that in the United States, contraceptives were commonly used to treat the symptoms of the disease but offered no real solution and had many undesirable side effects. I remembered his saying it was worth trying if you were seeking the contraceptive effect. So, I rejected the approach of the Tallahassee gynaecologist and declined to accept the prescription he had written for me. His acerbic remarks as we parted left me a little shaken. While I had confidently laid out my arguments in his office, I walked away fearing he might be right and that I might have ruined any hope for a family by not keeping the disease "at bay" sooner. After all, he was the one with the medical degree and specialized training and the consultations I'd had with British doctors on the subject were never very comprehensive.

As my appointment with Dr. Oliver approached, I feared that I would hear the same thing. The enormous relief I felt at learning there would be no awkward moments over family planning gave way to a long discussion about my concerns related to fertility. It was the first comprehensive discussion I'd had with any doctor about the nature of endometriosis and the first time I dealt with an American doctor who didn't have an agenda of convincing me to follow a particular line of treatment. Here were the options and possible outcomes laid out almost in a flow chart. It appealed to my academic mind set. He could promise little and in a gentle way confirmed what I already knew about the possible effects of the disease on my fertility. He indicated that generally it was recommended that couples try for a year to achieve a pregnancy before beginning an infertility investigation and explained the various steps this would entail if needed. I felt quite settled as I left the office. I was not eager to begin any medical investigations and was still hopeful that a baby would come in time. But, we had a plan in case that didn't work out.

As the months passed without a pregnancy, Gordon and I had been encouraged to pursue an infertility consultation through the organization from whom we learned the method of natural family planning. Our local teaching couple thought this might be helpful to us. This involved an extensive review of all the charts we had kept and a record of my daily diet, exercise and activities. The reply we received to our enquiry added a whole new dimension to the anguish we already felt. The solution to our infertility problem was to be found in more fervent prayer, a diet which consisted in less salad and more green vegetables, daily doses of flax seed oil, and the application of wild yam cream to the inside creases of my arms! Most of the letter was devoted to warning us not to seek medical treatment which could be immoral and above all the need for me to end my career: sentence after sentence about "full-time mothering" all of which seemed strangely insensitive as I was not a mother and it was unclear whether I could become one. The overall tone of the letter conveyed the author's deep disapproval of professional women and seemed to suggest that I did not deserve to be a mother. I felt somewhat brutalized by this letter in the same way I had been by the Tallahassee gynaecologist who had sought to exercise his brand of paternalism in attempting to "manage" my fertility.

After a year had elapsed with no sign of pregnancy, we went back to Dr. Oliver and began the preliminary tests. All the results looked promising but still there was no baby. At this point, he thought it appropriate to refer me to a gynaecologist. This suggestion filled me with trepidation. I did not want to see another gynaecologist. However, the monthly pattern of tremendous hope to be followed by a sense of grief when it was clear that I was again not pregnant was intensifying, and I knew I would need to overcome my fear of gynaecologists. Dr. Oliver indicated that there was someone in Tallahassee who had treated a lot of women with endometriosis and he might be able to help me. He also mentioned that we might want to consider seeking treatment at the Pope Paul VI Institute in Omaha,

Nebraska. He was leaving for a conference later that day at which Dr. Hilgers was due to speak and he was clearly excited about the trip. He told us about Dr. Hilgers's work and the high success rates he'd had in treating infertility. It rather took us by surprise but sounded like a very exciting prospect.

But Nebraska! Surely, there was someone nearer to Tallahassee who could do similar things. We couldn't understand why, if his techniques were so successful, others nearer to Tallahassee didn't use them. Still, we had Dr. Oliver write down all the contact details for the Pope Paul VI Institute. As we talked on the way home from Dr. Oliver's, we thought really it was best to go with the local doctor. We had from the very beginning agreed that we would not pursue extraordinary means to achieve a pregnancy; whether these be medical, financial or both. Our initial reaction was that treatment in Nebraska by a "star" gynaecologist would likely fall into the category of unreasonable expense. Perhaps it was not God's will that we should have a child. We needed to be open to this possibility. We had so much else to be grateful for. We had a wonderful marriage with so many shared interests and activities, friends and family, promising careers; a happy and very full life. We had talked about adoption. However, Gordon's immigration situation needed to be resolved before we put too much emotional energy into that idea.

When the day of my appointment with the local gynaecologist arrived, I was hopeful though nervous. Dr. Oliver had prepared me for the prospect that he might want to do a laparoscopy to check for endometriosis. I assumed we would have a discussion about my medical history and proceed with arrangements for a diagnostic laparoscopy. The appointment turned out to be one of the most stressful encounters of my life. Following his examination of my pelvis, he announced that I had a large "mass: that should be removed along with perhaps some of the bowel." He would make an appointment with a general surgeon for Monday. As for the endometriosis, yes, he was sure that I had extensive endometriosis and that it wasn't worth treating. My pelvis was more or less destroyed. He felt a pregnancy by natural means would be impossible. If we wanted a baby, we should go to the IVF clinic in Jacksonville.

I went to get Gordon from the waiting room. The doctor seemed to be saying that not only would I never have a baby but there was also something else seriously wrong with me that would require extensive surgery. I was in such a state of shock, I wasn't even sure I was taking in the information correctly. He explained the situation again to Gordon. I remember Gordon trying to comfort me as I was losing my battle to fight back the tears. The doctor seemed not to notice or perhaps it was easier to ignore me at that moment. He asked Gordon, "Do you have any children?" When Gordon replied "no," the doctor said, "So, we don't know if you work either." I left feeling like a heap of broken parts. I was also very agitated about the revelation of a "mass." We phoned Dr. Oliver even though it was the weekend. We had a long conversation about what had happened at the gynaecologist's office and he tried to reassure us that he had never felt any mass. He had us come on Monday morning to have another check. No, he couldn't feel anything. He couldn't reach the gynaecologist to get his account of what he thought was there. We left Dr. Oliver's feeling somewhat reassured that there was unlikely to be any problem that required the removal of a "mass" or part of the bowel. Still, the gynaecologist's words, "You will never get pregnant without the help of in vitro fertilization," rung in my head.

We had always opposed the option of in vitro fertilization. A large part of Gordon's teaching load at the university was ethics. We knew a great deal about the process, its abortifacient nature and its low success rate. I also remembered my feelings at reading an advertisement in my alumni magazine a few months earlier from a London fertility clinic. They were offering "generous remuneration" for eggs from women who had graduated from Oxford or Cambridge. I suppose I should have been flattered that my genetic material was so desirable, but I felt revulsion at the dehumanizing realization that parts of me could be sold as "spare parts." This was a whole world into which we were not spiritually or emotionally willing to enter.

After our disastrous visit to the gynaecologist in Tallahassee, things seemed more unresolved than before. I mentioned to a priest that I was dithering about whether to seek some further medical treatment out-of-state. He told me that "miracles do not happen until you have exhausted other means you have at your disposal, otherwise they would not be miracles." These words seemed to touch upon something that I hadn't realized until that moment. I did want to have closure in the sense that I had done all I could.

Still, I was nervous about the prospect of going to the Pope Paul VI Institute. Dr. Hilgers was after all, a gynaecologist, and I had become somewhat leery of any who would choose that medical specialty. I knew that many infertility specialists were careful in their selection of patients for fear of ruining their averages. Were his success rates due to a unique approach to infertility or were they a result of careful patient selection? What if he refused to treat me? I already had a history of stage IV endometriosis and was over 30. The gynaecologist in Tallahassee had already labeled me as hopeless. What if he was of a similar mindset to those at the natural family planning organization who disapproved of my professional life and the likelihood that I would continue working after we had children such that he would rather fill his schedule with someone else? I wasn't sure how I would cope emotionally with further rejection, but I decided to phone anyway. I was put in touch with one of Dr. Hilgers's nurses who explained the procedure for reviewing my charts and medical history. The warmth I felt in these early phone conversations with Institute staff gave me the confidence to follow through. I gathered our charts and other information and sent them off.

A letter from Dr. Hilgers came almost by return of post. Based on my medical history, he thought it reasonable to assume that I still had some endometriosis and adhesions. He spoke of these as "holding you back from an eventual successful pregnancy." Wow! "Eventual successful pregnancy." Those weren't really words I was expecting. I re-read the sentence so many times. I recognized how carefully chosen the words had been so as not to create unrealistic expectations. Still, it seemed so encouraging that he seemed eager to treat me. I hadn't been written off as not worth his time, likely to ruin his success rates or undeserving. Also, the cost of the treatment was comparable to what it would have been in Tallahassee.

From Dr. Oliver's first mention of the Pope Paul VI Institute, I had been gathering articles published by Dr. Hilgers both in medical journals and in Catholic venues. The more I read, the more comfortable I became. He seemed to hold out the promise of the most sophisticated medical techniques available, all within a context centered around the sacredness of human life, the primacy of God's creative power and the dignity of women. Having been reared in a family of scientists, I could not accept an uncritical rejection of modern science for fear that it could lead to moral danger. By the same token, Gordon and I recognized that not all that was technologically possible should be done. We wanted to pursue lines of treatment that were compatible with our moral beliefs. The philosophy of the Pope Paul VI Institute seemed neatly to encapsulate what we were looking for. Dr. Hilgers understood our profound desire for a child and willingness to apply his skills to remove any physical impediments. Yet, we also sensed a humility that knew that for all his talent, a child was a gift that could only come from God.

I went to Omaha in December 1998 to have the procedures Dr. Hilgers recommended: an ultrasound series, selective hysterosalpingogram, a laparoscopy and a comprehensive review of the results. The Institute was unlike any other doctor's office. There was something calming and affirming about even sitting in the waiting room. It was clear that an enormous amount of love and sacrifice had gone into its creation. I felt very privileged to be there. All the memories of previous visits to gynaecologists seemed to completely recede from my mind and I felt like we were starting anew.

The results of my laparoscopy revealed that I did have very extensive endometriosis and adhesions, but Dr. Hilgers was quite hopeful that they could be completely removed through further surgery. This, however, would be a major operation. He felt the endometriosis should be removed to improve my own health, regardless of our desire for children. I did experience quite a lot of chronic pain, though the memories of how excruciating the surgery done in England had been left me feeling that I might prefer to just live with it. He estimated the chances of a pregnancy after the second surgery to be 50 percent, possibly as good as 70 percent. This sounded very hopeful.

Dr. Hilgers left us to think about it and phone if we wanted to proceed. We decided not to make an immediate decision but take a few months to see if we could get pregnant without further help. It gave me time to steel up my courage to have the more extensive surgery. For someone used to the British National Health Service, Bergan Mercy Hospital in Omaha afforded a fair degree of culture shock. When I had the laparoscopy, the anesthesiologist had been so patient and careful in placing the IV line, the nurses so attentive and solicitous of my level of pain, and there was such a sense of privacy and individuality. It was a world away from the large wards, and somewhat dilapidated and understaffed hospitals in England.

Gordon and I went back to Nebraska the following summer to have the second surgery. There were some complications during the surgery, but it was deemed successful. I can remember driving back to Florida and feeling a profound sense of peace. I didn't know whether we would get pregnant in the months that lay ahead, but I could, for the first time place our desire for a baby solely in God's hands. We had done everything within our power and I trusted that whatever was to come was clearly His will for us. My prayer was no longer cluttered with fretful anxieties about discerning a way forward.

We learned of our pregnancy just as the first Sunday of Advent approached! A time of expectation and waiting that took on a whole new dimension for us. We made an appointment to see Dr. Oliver. I remember filling in the prenatal questionnaire and being asked, "Is this pregnancy a surprise?" Well, perhaps not in the way the question was intended, but it was, indeed, for us, a most extraordinary surprise. I repeated the home pregnancy test several times as if to make sure that the news was still true. A very early ultrasound showed the steady heartbeat of our son, James. We kept the photograph on our dresser for many months. The euphoric feeling continued throughout the pregnancy as we eagerly looked forward to the day we could hold the baby. The day (actually, wee hours of the morning) finally came. Here in my arms was a beautiful, healthy boy; the realization of so many prayers and dreams.

Our life with James has been indescribable. Three years on, I still marvel that we have this wonderful child. We soon began to imagine him with younger siblings and became eager for another pregnancy. This is proving no easier the second time around. In September 2003, we decided to seek some further advice from Dr. Hilgers, which led to minor surgery in November to clear up adhesions. We will see what happens. Again, I feel back in the place I was in July 1999. This time, we may not be blessed with a child, but I have a sense of joyful contentment with whatever may be God's will for us.

Institute Was the Right Choice for Us
Anonymous

Stan and I both come from large families (six kids in mine, five in his) and always knew that we'd love to have a big family of our own. Stan, an avid baseball fan, would comment that he wanted at least nine kids so that he could have his own baseball team!

We were married in May 1999. I was 30, Stan was 31, and we were anxious to start our family right away. Since we're both healthy we fully expected to be pregnant within the standard three to six months. When that didn't happen, I went to see an OB to be sure that everything was physically okay with me. My sisters and I have a history of severe menstrual cramps, but I didn't think much of it since some of them have children.

At my OB checkup, my doctor gave me the good news that everything was fine and that "the Big Guy and I just needed to get to work." After three or four more months of "work" and no results, I went back to the OB, who suggested a laparoscopy to check for endometriosis. I had feelings of total dread as they were wheeling me in for the surgery and explaining what the doctor would be doing. I was worried that he would take one or both of my ovaries, or even worse, my uterus. I made it through the laparoscopy, got the news that "everything was cleared up" and immediately decided that I needed to find a doctor whom I could trust.

After our first meeting at the Institute, I knew that it was the right choice for us. Their method demonstrates true respect for the patient, the married couple, and human life. I felt very confident in Dr. Hilgers. He really listened to what we said, had our best interest at heart, and was very honest with us in regard to my physical state and the chances of us conceiving.

At Dr. Hilgers's recommendation, I went for a second laparoscopy in June 2001. I remember waking up in the recovery room and Stan telling me that they were unable to do anything at that time because the endometriosis was so severe. At first I was so upset - how could it be "severe" when everything was supposedly cleared up just nine months prior? But, I resigned myself to the fact that I would be having major surgery the next month.

Fortunately, the surgery went very well, and shortly after I began taking medications to help improve my hormone levels. But months passed and we still did not conceive. Those were months of disappointment followed by feelings of guilt and failure. Becoming pregnant was supposed to be the easiest thing in the world, or so I was told. Throughout all of the disappointment, Dr. Hilgers and the staff at the Institute were exceptionally supportive and addressed both my physical and emotional concerns.

Even though Stan and I did not conceive as quickly as we hoped, it was reassuring to know that by using the **CREIGHTON MODEL Fer-tility*Care*™ System,** my overall health was also being evaluated. By following my cycle through charting and monthly reviews, we not only improved our chances of conceiving, but also treated concep-tion with the respect, dignity, and sanctity we believe it deserves.

Infertility affects many areas of your life. It is a strain emotion-ally, physically, and financially, not to mention the strain it can be on a couple's relationship. Stan and I have been blessed— and with the help of Dr. Hilgers, the staff at the institute, and many prayers, we are expecting our first child in a couple of months. Even when I write these words today it does not seem possible that after all we've been through, our dreams will come true.

The Greatest Christmas Present
We Ever Received
Agnes Machnik

My husband, Gregory, and I were married in August of 1995. We both came from Poland to live in the United States in 1993. Our journey to conception has been a long, uneasy one. When we got married, both at age 23, I never in the world would think how much time and courage it will take us to have a baby.

Two years after we married, I had to have a surgery that left me with only one ovary and one fallopian tube. I had a huge ovarian cyst that was removed along with my left ovary. I realized then that our chance of conceiving had slightly diminished. Then I learned more devastating news after I had a hysterosalpingography done. My only remaining tube was blocked. Our chances of conceiving decreased significantly. I was heartbroken. I asked my doctor who had removed my cyst, why he didn't try to open my right tube since he saw it was blocked. He responded to me that he tried but it did not work. Afterwards he told me that in order for me to have a baby I should have in vitro Fertilization done as soon as possible. He gave me a referral to a fertility clinic. I never called there nor went back to see this doctor again.

Around May 1999, my friend from New Jersey told me about the **CREIGHTON MODEL FertilityCare™ System** she heard about from her sister's friends who live in Canada. I learned that this is a natural method that helps to achieve or to avoid pregnancy. My husband and I did practice NFP, however we never learned the method, so I figured it would be beneficial for us to learn the **CREIGHTON MODEL**.

We went to see an instructor in upstate New York who introduced us to the **CREIGHTON MODEL** and showed us how to chart. We were excited to learn about different mucus patterns and what they meant. After two cycles of charting, we were able to send the chart and my medical records to Pope Paul VI Institute in Omaha and have them evaluated by Dr. Hilgers. This was really important to us, to have a very meaningful evaluation done of my present cycles and my past medical history. At that time I had extensive tail-end brown bleeding and very prolonged premenstrual brown bleeding as well. This started sometime after the first surgery. Doctor Hilgers recommended a few procedures, some to evaluate my hormone profile and some to evaluate and repair my fallopian tube. I learned from Doctor Hilgers that according to my medical records, the procedure that was used to open my tube most likely left more scarring that I had before the surgery.

The hormone profile could be arranged locally, the rest of the procedures would need to be done at the Pope Paul VI Institute. This meant a trip to Omaha. Both tasks were uneasy to accomplish; finding a lab in Queens, New York that could do the hormone profile, and making a decision to go to Omaha to have a surgery.

At last, after a few months of trying several labs and being refused, I found a hospital that agreed to draw and centrifuge my blood for the 11 times during my cycle, before and after ovulation. I'd had a serious talk with the financial director who finally agreed that if I prepaid for all the blood draws and had the lab director agree for me to come for so many times, then they would do it. The lab director agreed and I had my blood drawn.

My husband and I are self employed, and we usually are having a hard time getting good health insurance. We knew we needed the type of insurance that would have out-of-network coverage. We got the insurance we wanted and began planning a trip to Omaha in the spring of 2001. After the review of my chart and arrangements made with the nurses at the Pope Paul VI Institute and Bergen Mercy Hospital, my surgery was scheduled for June 02, 2001.

We were planning to take a vacation for three weeks and drive to Omaha. A few weeks before our trip I received a letter that I would no longer have any health insurance. Unfortunately everything had to be cancelled. I was devastated again; what an inconvenience. We had to start all over again. In the Fall of 2001 we found another insurance company that provided some out-of-network coverage.

Everything was arranged again and the surgery was scheduled for the second time for Tuesday March 19, 2002; day 10 of my cycle.

This meant that the latest I could get my period was March 10th. I have a history of irregular cycles, some cycles as long as 40-50 days. It was Sunday, March 10th and my period did not come. We were supposed to be leaving on Saturday, March 16th. I knew if my period did not come today we could not go to Omaha. It did come! We knew we were going. We drove there and on Monday, one day before the surgery, we met with Doctor Hilgers. He explained to us what he was going to do during the surgery. The surgery went well. My uterus, ovary and tube were cleaned from extensive adhesions I'd had for a long time, even before the first surgery.

Ten days later, on March 29th, which I remember was Good Friday, I had a laparoscopy done to take a second look at my pelvic area and to remove Gore-Tex, a surgical blanket that covered my uterus and the tube. Then the dye was injected into my right tube to see if it was unblocked. The dye spilled freely at the end of the tube. It meant that the tube was workable.

After the surgery I felt like we accomplished something remarkable. To drive 1,500 miles each way, stay there for over two weeks and have everything possible done during those two weeks gave us hope that we could conceive. Another milestone had been accomplished.

After we returned home, I found a letter from our health insurance company, saying that my out-of-network coverage terminated as of April 01, 2002. This time it really didn't matter anymore. We had made the trip to Pope Paul VI Institute.

After the surgery I was on Clomid and mucus-enhancing medication for a couple of months. I had no more tail-end brown bleeding and the prolonged premenstrual brown spotting was gone, too.

Four months after I stopped taking all medication we conceived. It is our miracle and the greatest Christmas present we have ever received. We found out that we were pregnant two days before Christmas of 2003. Right now, I am under the care of the Pope Paul VI Institute. I am having progesterone injections twice a week and have my progesterone monitored and checked every other week.

Our baby is due August 24, 2004. We are so grateful for everything that has happened to us, for nothing that happened was coincidence. Everything in life is according to a plan, but not our plan, God's plan.

More Physicians Should Understand the CrMS
Mia Moran-Cooper

In late summer of 2000, when a friend learned that my husband and I were trying to conceive a child, she introduced me to the **CREIGHTON MODEL FertilityCare™ System** and shared information regarding the local FertilityCare Center. She and her husband had been trying for many years to conceive, using a variety of methods, and this was what they had decided to stick with. She showed me their charts and it looked a little intimidating. Since my husband and I had just been trying for a few months and were only 38 years old, I basically shrugged it off and figured it would happen for us soon without all the little colored stickers! Besides, I had already started fertility treatment with my OB/GYN who had promised to refer me to a fertility specialist if she couldn't help within a few months.

Several months later, when we still hadn't conceived, we saw a small advertisement for FertilityCare in our church bulletin and attended the orientation session. It was conducted by a nurse practitioner whom I had gone through 12 years of school with! I was a little uncomfortable at first, but her level of professionalism and true concern for our situation helped alleviate that. She was warm, supportive and so knowledgeable. She explained to me that the Pope Paul VI Institute looked at infertility as the "tip of the iceberg," not the problem itself, but rather the symptom of other underlying health problems, which if treated, will result in a healthier woman much more likely to conceive.

After a few months, Dr. Hilgers reviewed my charts and replied with a letter, outlining numerous reasons he suspected contributed to my infertility, including endometriosis and a hormonal imbalance. He recommended a laparoscopy, a series of blood tests and preferrably a trip out to Omaha. Instead, we decided to have as much done here as we could. Interestingly, when my local doctor did my laparoscopy, she found endometriosis, although I had no physical symptoms. I think she was as surprised as I was, yet I recalled Dr. Hilgers's letter predicting it; all based on those little stickers!

Unfortunately, our friends still hadn't conceived and we kept our doctor's referral to a fertility specialist after a six-month wait. During the first visit, we showed him the series of blood work that Dr. Hilgers had ordered, thinking he would want to know what another physician had ordered. Instead, he mocked the papers, saying "How much are they charging you for this in the name of the Church?" We felt humiliated, but at age 39, we were desperate, so we tolerated the sarcasm and began a series of artificial inseminations. On the fourth round, with no success, his nurse offered to let my husband depress the plunger saying, "Now you can feel like you are part of this." It was gross, barbaric and it was at this moment that we understood why our Church teaches us that this is wrong. There was nothing sacred in that act; nor her attitude! Luckily, we had continued following the FertilityCare System and charting and we had a greater appreciation for the dignity and sanctity of the human body!

As my 40th birthday rolled around, we began to look into adoption. Then our friends shared their joyous news; after nine years, they had conceived! Our faith in the method was re-ignited, and we made the trip to Omaha at the end of July and were impressed with what a holy place it was. When I checked in at the local hospital so Dr. Hilgers could repeat the laparoscopy, even the admissions clerk spoke of him with a tone of awe! She said people from all over the USA traveled there for his help, and his success was well known.

At the end of our visit, he provided me with an aggressive treatment regimen of vitamins, hormones and even a new thyroid pill. He said he wished he had seen us sooner, because of my age, he only gave me a 35%-40 percent odds of conception and asked that I give his treatment one year! If nothing else, I would become a healed, healthy, balanced woman. We left a dozen roses at the foot of the statue of St. Therese and thanked God for having led us to such a wonderful man and his staff.

That Fall, we became godparents to our friend's son, a little Pope Paul VI Institute miracle. In the following year, as I followed his recommendations, I became a healed woman. My PMS, which was often severe, disappeared. Mood swings were gone, and I lost weight that I had struggled with for years. I had more energy, and I felt better than I ever had in my life. My husband swore that even if we never conceived, he wanted me to stay on Dr. Hilgers's plan!

As the one-year anniversary of our trip to Omaha approached, we were sad that we had not yet conceived yet we were at peace that we had done all we could. We met with the FertilityCare nurse on Tuesday and she encouraged us to go the distance just a little longer, but we told her we would have to think about it. Imagine our surprise when three days later, we discovered we were expecting. Our miracle had indeed been performed!

The Institute has followed us carefully these past nine months, supplementing progesterone to ward off miscarriage or pre-term birth. At 42 years of age, people just assume we had in vitro fertilization, and I am delighted to share our story of the Institute and our local FertilityCare program. The current concept of just giving a woman a baby through alternative methods without treating her underlying problems seems reprehensible to us now.

Our first child (and at our age, probably our last!) was born on April 6, 2004, just a few days ahead of her due date. She was 20 inches long and weighed 6 lb. 12 oz. It was love at first sight. We gave her the name of Cana, after the wedding feast where Christ performed His first miracle; turning water into wine. We believe she is our miracle. Her middle name is Rose, for a variety of reasons. It was our good friend, Rose, who first introduced us to the local FertilityCare program when we had difficulty conceiving. Another is that we had asked for the intercession of St. Therese to pick for us a "heavenly rose" and send it, and she certainly did! The first saint of the Americas was St. Rose of Lima, Peru, and of course as a tribute to our Emerald Isle heritage, she is our Wild Irish Rose!

Every day we marvel in the miracle of her and thank God for the work of Dr. Hilgers and his staff and affiliates. Without his help, we are certain to have remained childless. In gratitude, we have pledged to do all we can to support and promote the Institute and local FertilityCare Center. We will start by creating a Web site where others can access information and local success stories can be shared. I will try to get more media interest in our local program as well as for the Institute and Dr. Hilgers's book. The bottom line is that we are humbled to have been blessed by such a miracle as Cana Rose. Thank you and may God bless you all!

Every Child is God's Miracle
Anonymous

In 1990, my husband had a vasectomy. Our reason for having this procedure was due to my history of high risk pregnancies. I had lost a baby girl during my sixth month of pregnancy; her name was Hope. She died two days after the premature delivery. My doctor had no real explanation for the early birth.

Approximately two years after losing my baby girl, I became pregnant with my second daughter, who was also exposed to the same risk and danger. During my seventh month I had gone into labor, but thank goodness for the use of a generic drug called Yutopar, which prevented labor and kept me pregnant full term. On the advice of my OB physician, he suggested I not have any more children, due to the high risks involved. I was devastated that I should not conceive again.

Years later my husband joined the Catholic Church and learned that a vasectomy was against the Catholic faith. He had a strong desire to have a reversal, and we realized it was God's decision if we should have more children. So we placed matters in God's hands, had the reversal and tried to conceive.

For the first couple of years we tried on our own, to no avail. Heartbroken and desperate, we began searching for another way. We looked into in vitro fertilization and considered it an option. We even discussed this matter with several priests and finally found one who told us it was acceptable as long as it was us and not from an outside donor. (We discovered later it is not accepted by the Catholic Church)?

We made an appointment with a fertility specialist and arranged for in vitro fertilization, a very costly procedure and one that our insurance did not cover. We tried this method and it failed. At this point I was a total basket case. I was driven to have a child and would have done anything to conceive. Many prayers, rosaries and novenas were said and still no baby. I began to wonder if it was me and not my husband.

Through God's guidance, we were led to the **CREIGHTON MODEL FertilityCare™ System**. We knew the nurse who headed the program and trusted her good advice. We learned the method quickly and began the charting process. Oh, the endless charting! It seemed as though each month's end brought more tears and pain as I did not conceive. Our local nurse suggested that Dr. Hilgers at the Pope Paul VI Institute review all my charts and past pregnancy medical records. Dr. Hilgers also requested a hormonal series of blood work. This actually brought much information. It was discovered that my progesterone levels were very low and this may have been the cause for my past premature pregnancy problems. Finally I got an answer for the cause of the high risk pregnancies!

Dr. Hilgers suggested I take Clomid and continue the blood tests to check my hormone levels. In addition to this, I was taking prenatal vitamins, Vitamin B6, along with injections each month. My husband was taking Proxeed, a drug to increase sperm motility/mobility. We continued to periodically have a semen analysis, which revealed my husband's sperm count to drastically fall and rise at times. We were at the end of our rope when told that we had less than a ten percent chance of conceiving. I was on my last month of Clomid and began to believe we would never get pregnant. Although our hope began to waver, we still continued to try.

As it turned out, through our own efforts coupled, with the **CREIGHTON MODEL FertilityCare™ System** and **NaProTECHNOLOGY,** we finally conceived. When I found out I was pregnant, I was truly amazed! After all these years of trying and being 39 years old, it truly was a miracle. The odds were totally against us; considering my age, my husband's low sperm count and my low progesterone. I do feel fortunate that I finally became pregnant.

During my pregnancy, I was advised by Dr. Hilgers to continue monitoring my progesterone levels with bi-weekly blood tests. I was taking progesterone supplements and being very careful during the pregnancy.

On October 11, 2002, I delivered a full term healthy baby boy. We proudly named him Thomas Patrick and what a joy he has been! God has truly blessed us, and we have so many to thank. There were numerous friends and family members praying for us and many people we did not even know. Through prayer and perseverance, our little miracle son came to be.

I want to thank God Almighty for our gift of life. I also want to thank Dr. Hilgers, his staff and nurses, and all our friends and family for all their help, support and prayers. A good friend of mine gave me a picture frame gift for our son, which is inscribed, "Every Child is God's Miracle." How true. Thank you, Jesus!

We Found Doctor with the Right Knowledge and Skills
Kristi Scheele

My story begins in February of 1974 when my husband, Fred, and I were married. We were in our mid-20s and were ready for a family, so we started trying to have a baby within three months. Nothing happened! I was so disappointed month after month, as I had always wanted to have two or three children by the time I was 30. Here I was 27 and NOT pregnant. Being a Registered Nurse, I knew it was time to seek help. I saw an OB/GYN doctor who did several tests, but no real problems were uncovered. So, the next step was for my husband to be tested. The urologist told us not to plan on having any children of our own because my husband had a very low sperm count. We were devastated! I felt so badly for Fred because he was the one that really wasn't keen on adoption. Just imagine how we felt two weeks later when I found out I was pregnant. At first we could not believe it, but then came the debilitating morning sickness that lasted five months. The rest of my pregnancy was uneventful, and I delivered our beautiful daughter, Karla Janiece Scheele on September 23, 1976. She weighed 9 pounds 6 1/2 ounces, was 21 inches long and had a full head of pretty dark curly hair.

After Karla was born, we thought the problem was fixed — WRONG! We started trying for another baby when Karla was just a few months old, and for years after that, nothing happened. My biological clock was ticking!! In 1980 I saw a fertility specialist in Lincoln. He ran several tests including a laparoscopy, which showed I had endometriosis. He prescribed Danazol for six months to try to get rid of it. I thought after that I would conceive. But, again nothing happened. I was a mess because all I saw when I was out were pregnant women, and all the "well meaning" people around us kept saying to "relax, at least you have Karla!" It just wasn't that simple!

Finally a friend of mine told me about a fertility specialist by the name of Dr. Thomas Hilgers at Creighton University Medical Center in Omaha. So, I made an appointment with him in March of 1982. My husband and I made the trip to Omaha, only to find that it would take several months for the evaluation. I tried to convince Dr. Hilgers to "speed-up" the process, but he was emphatic about his "routine." I came home and cried for days!! Having no other option at this point we made another appointment and started Dr. Hilgers's evaluation. During the next two months I made several trips to Omaha for tests. In June, another laparoscopy showed mild to moderate endometriosis and if I was going to have a chance to become pregnant again, I would need surgery to remove it. I was NOT fond of the idea of major surgery. You know us nurses, we know too much! However, my husband convinced me it would be OK and that this was our only hope of having more children.

The first part of August I had the surgery. It was a success and I recovered well. As soon as Dr. Hilgers thought I was completely healed, he started me on Clomid to stimulate ovulation. He told us that for some reason anovulatory cycles go with endometriosis but it is a puzzle as to which comes first. (In other words the proverbial "which comes first the chicken or the egg" concept.) We did ultrasounds every month; and I was ovulating, but nothing happened so he changed medication and put me on Pergonal. I did ovulate several eggs each month with this medication, and in February of 1983, it looked like I was pregnant. However, it turned out to be a blighted ovum. I was sad and depressed, but kept trying.

In April my period did not come, so I made an appointment with Dr. Hilgers. The day I went to have a pregnancy test done, Dr. Hilgers was out of the office. I was disappointed I did not get to see him. But the nurses called him and he ordered the pregnancy test. When they called me back to get the results, I remember them saying Dr. Hilgers wanted to talk to me on the phone. They had "strict instructions" to have me sit in his chair in his office to take the call. I said "Are you sure this is OK?" they said "Oh yes, this is what he told us to do!" So, I sat in his chair and answered the phone. He asked if I was sitting down and I told him I was. He then told me we indeed were going to have a "Christmas baby." I kind of knew I was pregnant, but having so many problems along the way, it took a few minutes to "sink in." We were very cautious the first few months as my progesterone level was a little low. I took progesterone shots, and had ultrasounds done on a regular basis to check on the baby. After about three months my hormone levels were better and we breathed a little easier. Seeing the baby on ultrasound made it "real" to us and we were elated! I actually felt great and had no problems with the pregnancy after that and the delivery also went well, even though I had a long labor. Kevin Harris-Otto Scheele was born December 30, 1983. He weighed 8 pounds 11 3/4 ounces and was 20 inches long. We were so happy to have a daughter and now a son! Kevin was the first grandson on both sides, so that was special, too.

Since Dr. Hilgers had given us so much encouragement and medical help, it would have been nice to have him deliver Kevin. But, we live two hours from Omaha, and being winter, we knew that was not feasible. This turned out to be a very good decision because we had a lot of snow and blowing snow in December of 1983. Therefore, our family doctor, David Demuth, delivered Kevin at the York Hospital. I cannot say enough good things about Dr. Hilgers and Dr. Demuth as they truly helped us during this extremely difficult time. They were so compassionate, understanding and willing to work with us. We are very grateful to both of them.

This in itself is a wonderful story, however our story does not end here. Do you remember how I had wanted at least three children? With all we had been through, we did not think I could get pregnant again without more surgery and medications. Well, God had other ideas, and in May of 1985 I found out I was pregnant for the third time. My progesterone level was very high this time, so everything looked good for a full term pregnancy. And indeed it was! Kyle Fred-Harris Scheele arrived on December 28, 1985. He weighed 9 pounds 5 ounces and was 20 inches long. How thrilled we were to have a daughter and two sons!!! Even though I was 37 (7 years later than I had wanted), our family was complete. How blessed we are to have three healthy children!! Especially when back in 1975 we were told we would never have children of our own. Just goes to show, never say never!

As you might well guess the emotional "roller coaster" of all this was not easy. Some days I just did not know what to do. I remember sitting at the kitchen table early in the morning one day, reading my Daily Guidepost, fighting back the tears. I was depressed and frustrated. I prayed to God to somehow let me know if we were doing the right thing. Then a voice in my head said, "Yes! You are on the right track". That gave me hope that we were supposed to pursue having more children. Plus, the support of my friend and prayer partner Dianne really helped get me through each day. Fortunately, my husband was very supportive and we handled it all as a team. I felt very lucky, and still do, that he remained by my side through all the ups and downs. Because statistics show that infertility is very hard on a marriage and many break up because of it. Luckily we were not a statistic and just celebrated our 30th anniversary on February 8, 2004.

The hours spent in the waiting room each month turned out to be a blessing. We developed some wonderful new friendships, which turned out to be our "built-in" support group. Even our husbands got to know each other and the ten of us got together several times over the course of the next three years. One of the women in the group, Nancy, and I became so close that when both of us needed surgery for endometriosis, we decided we should go to the hospital together. We even got Dr. Hilgers to arrange for us to be roommates, which was not easy, as he said that "just wasn't done". But he did, and it certainly made the hospital stay easier, since my husband could not be there every day. Nancy and I still correspond every Christmas.

Our story is unique, but I know there are many other wonderful stories. Looking at Karla, Kevin and Kyle now, all that we went through seems like a dream or another lifetime. And thinking back on all the tests, the "hundreds" of trips to Omaha, the surgeries, the emotions, and all the money we spent. (some $25,000, which seems like a small amount compared to what the costs are today). I really do not know how we coped with it all. However, I do know that I never considered giving up. I knew in my heart that it would happen, If we found the right doctor with the right knowledge and skills. And we did! We are truly thankful for Dr. Hilgers and his expertise, which facilitated God's miracle of pregnancy and birth.

Twenty Years of Love, Patience and Kindness at Institute
Teresa Schwietz

Where does one begin to explain my gratitude for what I have received? It started in 1981 when I was diagnosed with endometriosis. I was told that I would have to have a hysterectomy. But first it was suggested I see Dr. Thomas Hilgers for a second opinion.

Honestly, at first I wasn't too sure how he could change this diagnosis, amazingly I was wrong. First they were able to get me off the pill which I hated taking due to being Catholic. I was told I had to do this because of my diagnosis. That is where my husband, Mark, and I were introduced to **THE CREIGHTON MODEL Fertility*Care*™ System** in place of taking the pill. I was told from previous doctors that the pill was going to be the only cure as well as the hysterectomy.

I remember how nervous I was on our first visit, wanting to be excited, yet holding myself down. He went over a few options for both of us and told us what we might be up against. However, Mark and I felt in our hearts we had to try all options. We began with ultrasounds, and for two years I tried several medications. I also had three laparoscopies, and Dr. Hilgers sat down with us afterwards to go over the videotape of my surgery to show us what he had done. At first I thought there is no way I will be able to watch that, but what an experience! Things began to make some sense to both of us.

The emotional ups and downs were incredible. We'd wonder if this month would be different because painful intercourse was affecting us as a couple. Mark and I decided to keep trying, but at the same time decided to start the adoption process.

I remember going every month for about six months for two weeks at a time to drink gallons of water to prepare for the ultrasound each day to determine ovulation (I was also diagnosed with no ovulation). This, on top of the endometriosis, was making things more difficult. Many months I would go three to four months without menstruation and think "this is it!" only to be disappointed again and then having to get that "dreadful" progesterone shot. I would have a talk with my "hips" that this would be the last month!

I remember the week I found out I was pregnant with my daughter. Our dog had just died, and I was devastated. My father told me, "Teresa, something bigger will replace this." At the time I didn't understand, but very shortly it all came together. My husband and I had gone to the adoption agency again and were told they had nothing at that time but we would stay on the list. I left there and went to the Institute to get my blood work done again, before my shot. I waited for the blood work so I wouldn't have to go back later to receive the shot. Oh my gosh, the girls came out so excited to say, I was pregnant! I called Mark. He was on a roof at work but I told his boss this was an EMERGENCY! We drove from Omaha to Sioux City, Iowa that night to tell my folks.

Things went along fairly well. I had to keep track of times for shots and ultrasounds. At five months along, Mark and I were driving home from Des Moines when I had the worst stomach pains. The cramps would come and go. The next morning I went to work and still felt the same, and since I worked at Creighton University Pediatrics Department at the time, I mentioned it to the doctors there. They immediately sent me to labor and delivery. The baby decided she wanted to come and join the party! I was put in the hospital and they did a cervical cerclage. For the next four months I would receive two shots of progesterone twice a week in each hip. Around July 30th, they clipped my cervix and we all thought I would go into labor right away, WRONG! Finally, on August 14, 1986, our daughter, Kaitlin, was born after 22 hours of labor.

After about six months of getting the hang of being a parent, going back to work and settling into life, I thought that my endometriosis would have been done, at least I hoped so. It wasn't; and the journey began again.

I went for another surgery, and my appendix had to be removed at the same time. After that surgery, however, I had complications. I was home recovering and I collapsed, and Mark took me to the Pope Paul VI Institute. They rushed me over to Bergan Mercy Hospital where tests began. It was noted that I had a blood clot. I became extremely weak and they were preparing me for surgery again. I remember waking up at one point and Dr. Hilgers was sitting by my bedside. His care for his patients was incredible. My mother contacted the Carmelites in Iowa for prayer. By the next day, my clot had shrunk, my coloring was much better, and I was released a few days later. I can honestly say that was the one time in my life I was actually scared for myself and for my daughter.

I continued to keep trying for another pregnancy. In September of 1989, I found out I was pregnant with my second child. Things were going pretty good until September 29th when I started spotting. October 1st was the Feast of St. Therese and also the blessing for expectant parents. I wanted to be blessed, so after much convincing, Mark took me to Mass and I came back to rest. Later that night, however, I lost a lot of blood.

I called Dr. Hilgers and he thought I had probably miscarried. I stayed in bed for several days and then went back to work. About a week later, my breasts started to hurt again, I felt sick to my stomach and thought, "What is wrong with me?" I went to the Institute for an ultrasound to make sure I didn't need a D&C but lo and behold, I was still pregnant. WOW! I was so excited. Again on the ultrasound you could see what looked like a large clot above the sac of the baby. I had gotten a second opinion on the whole situation, and one called it a "vanishing twin." I still don't know what the whole thing was, I call it a MIRACLE!

I was bedridden for the next three months until the clot shrunk enough that I was out of danger. My co-workers were incredible and would bring me work and administer my shots weekly. Each week I would get another ultrasound to check the status of the baby. This time required many prayers and much patience.

Dr. Hilgers and I set the C-Section for May 15, 1990. Because I was high risk and worked for the Neonatalogists at Creighton Medical Center, I wanted very much to be there. Dr. Hilgers had not delivered there in years but agreed to my request.

During the C-Section I could feel the whole thing. I had an awesome crew, especially those I worked with. Mark was able to be there the whole time (last time he wasn't because they put me completely out). Adam was born weighing 8 lb.

My sister was living with us during this time which was a blessing. Mark traveled a lot and her help and inspiration during the pregnancy and after was incredible. Then we were transferred to Minnesota; I commuted from Minnesota to Omaha for my check-ups. In October of 1991, I had another miscarriage. I was beginning to not like October anymore.

In 1993, we moved from Minnesota to Arizona. I continued to go in for my check-ups each December. In 1997, the pain began to be greater, so Mark and I went to a local women's clinic to see what could be done here rather than traveling back to Omaha. What a mistake! The bedside manner of this physician was incredible - not even a hello – just "What is your problem?" He suggested I have an ultrasound and sent me over to radiology. It showed fibroid tumors. The radiologist was concerned, so he called the physician who said he'd see me again in six months or so. I was leaving for Ireland in about three weeks and the pain and bleeding was a constant issue. I called the Pope Paul VI Institute and they suggested I fax the report, which I did. We then hopped on a plane to Omaha within a few days to visit with Dr. Hilgers. Again, a miracle for me. Dr. Hilgers had just trained a physician who lived in Ireland, and if I had any problems while there I could contact him. At the time, Dr. Hilgers suggested I also think about a hysterectomy because the bleeding that was becoming worse along with the back pain was really slowing me down. Fortunately, the trip to Ireland was a success.

Finally, in November of 1998, I made the difficult decision to have the hysterectomy. I opted to fly back to Omaha to have Dr. Hilgers perform the surgery. It was a matter of confidence and trust. I remember the day before the surgery; he asked me again if I felt comfortable with my decision, and I said I was.

The surgery went well. I stayed in Sioux City, Iowa with my folks for the next five days before I was to fly home. However, four days following surgery I started having horrible cramping, so I went back to the Institute to be checked. It was discovered that I had a blood clot which was causing my pain. I went back to Iowa for four more days to recover. Finally I flew back to Arizona and stayed on bed rest for the next six weeks; not an easy chore for me! I continued to have cramping off and on for the next six months because the blood clot persisted. Now, five years later, I am doing well. I have been on Triestrogen for the past five years. It works well for me.

Every Christmas when I go home to visit my family in Iowa, I schedule my yearly check-up at the Institute because I feel totally taken care of. I believe God sent an angel to me, and for that I will be forever grateful to Dr. Hilgers and his incredible staff for the love, patience and kindness over the past 20 years!

Through God's Grace, We are Now a Family
Gina Smiskey

Rachel is our 18-month-old daughter. She is the answer to many prayers, and she would not be here if it weren't for Dr. Hilgers and the Pope Paul VI Institute. Like many young couples, we married shortly after college and took life for granted. We assumed that we would be able to have children when we were ready. This is where our journey began and now looking back, although it was difficult, we have grown so much by our struggles, and we are a closer family and have a stronger faith in God because of these tough times.

Sean, my husband, was diagnosed with testicular cancer at the age of 29. It was quite a shock as no one in his family had ever had this disease. With God's grace Sean was healed, and we decided it was time for us to start a family. We anticipated the exciting time when we would be able to share with our friends and family the good news that a baby was on the way. Several months went by and still nothing. We had been practicing the sympto-thermal method of natural family planning, and we continued to chart, assuming that we would soon be pregnant. In August 2000, one year after Sean's cancer diagnosis, we had a positive pregnancy test and were elated. We told everyone because we were so excited. Seven weeks into the pregnancy I started developing some complications, but my local doctors said there was nothing that could be done, so we had to wait things out. In late September, we lost our first baby to a miscarriage. This was the most devastating personal event that I have ever had to live through. We wanted a baby for so long and then we went from being so happy to so sad and depressed in a number of days.

We continued on and tried to heal, although I don't think I ever really recovered from that loss. That baby still holds a special place in our life and we know that Jesus is taking good care of her up in heaven. In the spring of 2001 after six more months of trying to conceive again, we found out about the Pope Paul VI Institute. We began taking classes to learn the **CREIGHTON MODEL FertilityCare™ System** and we finally had hope that Dr. Hilgers could help us carry a pregnancy to term.

After looking at three months of charting, Dr. Hilgers was able to tell that I had an ovulatory dysfunction and possibly endometriosis. This initial diagnosis was made before even meeting me in person. I was amazed at the **CREIGHTON MODEL** and how much the charting could reveal about a woman's cycle. I began a month-long hormone evaluation where blood was drawn and sent to the lab in Omaha. More information concluded that I have polycystic ovarian disease, which prevents me from ovulating. We scheduled an appointment to see Dr. Hilgers and we drove from Wisconsin to Omaha in June 2001.

While in Omaha I went through ultrasounds and then a procedure called a diagnostic laparoscopy and selective hysterosal-pingogram. This revealed that my tubes were clear but that my ovaries were 2 ½ times the size of normal ovaries, hence the reason I was not ovulating. Dr. Hilgers was not confident that ovulation-inducing medications would help in our situation, but we went home to try Clomid for six cycles to see what would happen, and then if needed, we would discuss other options.

Three cycles dragged on with tears and hopelessness starting to set in. We had already been through so much that each month when I wasn't pregnant just hit harder and harder and we kept questioning whether or not God wanted us to be parents. Then after the fourth round of Clomid, I was out of town on business and was continuing to chart my cycle. I was instructed by Dr. Hilgers's nurses that if I reached Peak + 16 days that I should take a pregnancy test and if it was positive to contact them right away. I was alone in my hotel room that night when I took the pregnancy test and it was positive. I was so excited I could hardly keep myself from getting in the car and driving four hours home to tell Sean. I got myself together and called Dr. Hilgers's office and was immediately put on progesterone injections following a baseline progesterone test.

Dr. Hilgers carefully monitored my progesterone levels throughout my pregnancy. We now know that low progesterone levels are probably the reason we lost our first baby. We knew we were in good hands, and I continued to have faith that this baby would be born healthy.

On June 24, 2002, Rachel Marie Smiskey was born weighing 6 lb. 9 oz. She was healthy as can be and has brought true joy to our lives. We don't go a day without thanking the Lord for her life and for leading us to Dr Hilgers. The technology that the **CREIGHTON MODEL Fertility*Care*™ System** and the Pope Paul VI Institute have developed is amazing and helped us become a family. We were a married couple prior to this, but now we are a family. In fact, we are a family that is expecting another little miracle on July 4, 2004. Once again, with Dr. Hilgers's help, we have another healthy pregnancy.

Just four years ago, we weren't sure where our lives were heading. We were lost and confused. All we wanted was to be parents. Now we know how precious life is, and Rachel and our new baby are the miracles that many take for granted. We are forever grateful to Dr. Hilgers for making this family complete!

Progesterone Treatment Led to Our Healthy Baby Boy
Annette Sughroue

My husband and I had been trying for two years to have a baby with no success. I knew that I needed to know why I wasn't able to get pregnant. My prayers were answered when I was directed to Dr. Hilgers, director of the Pope Paul VI Institute in Omaha, Nebraska.

I was told that prior to meeting with him I had to learn the **CREIGHTON MODEL Fertility*Care*™ System**. There wasn't anyone in my area who could teach this system to me, so I found a FertilityCare Practitioner back in my hometown who was willing to do this for me via telephone.

I charted my cycles for two months and then sent my chart to Dr. Hilgers. He in turn reviewed my charts and wrote me a letter describing what he thought was wrong. He thought that I had polycystic ovarian disease (PCOD).

So, in October 1999 I went to Omaha and Dr. Hilgers performed a laparoscopy to be sure. Then I went back in December 1999 to have major surgery to remove the cysts that were on my ovaries. After the surgery Dr. Hilgers also thought that I had a slight case of endometriosis.

In April 2000 I went back to the Pope Paul VI Institute and saw Dr. Hilgers for a follow-up visit. During this visit he wanted to start testing my progesterone level because he thought that I might not be ovulating. I had my blood drawn near my home every other week for approximately a month and I would send the sample to the lab in Omaha.

There was no change in my progesterone level and I had not started my period yet either. On May 17, 2000 the lab decided to do a pregnancy test, and that same day Linda, Dr. Hilgers's head nurse called to tell me that I was pregnant! The tears welled up in my eyes and I immediately left work to tell my husband. We were so excited!

Linda told me that since my progesterone level was so low I needed to start receiving injections of natural progesterone two times a week until my progesterone increased to an acceptable level. As it turned out I had to get the injections for the remainder of my pregnancy. I also went back to Omaha for ultrasounds twice.

I believe that my risk of having a miscarriage would have been very high had I not used the natural progesterone. Happily, on December 21, 2000 I gave birth to a full-term healthy baby boy.

Institute Helped Me Let Go and Let God Lead My Life
Shelly Theil

Infertility? I'd never thought about it. My plan was to just let things happen, but after a year of nothing happening, I started to get worried. My husband's reaction was "Everything's fine. Quit worrying!" But I couldn't quit. All my friends were starting to have babies, and I felt I was ready.

My cousin suggested taking Natural Family Planning classes. Of course, as a lifelong Catholic, I'd heard about Natural Family Planning through church and school, but I always thought one used it to postpone pregnancy, not plan one. I visited with my gynecologist about it. His reaction was "Women have been getting pregnant for thousands of years without charting – don't waste your time with it." But we went anyway. Within one month of using NFP, we were pregnant! We were so excited, and I couldn't wait to wear maternity clothes, plan the nursery, and pick out names.

At about twelve weeks, a few days before my first appointment, I started to bleed. It was the weekend. They told me to lie down and take it easy and come in for an ultrasound on Monday. I thought, "This can't be happening." Then the tech said, "I'm sorry to tell you this, especially with a first pregnancy, but I'm not finding a heartbeat."

The doctor was very kind. He told us that we could try again in three months. They didn't know why it happened, but that it happens to a lot of women. It isn't until after the loss of three babies that they do any testing to see what's going on. "We have to have three miscarriages before they do tests to see if something's wrong with me?" I thought. I didn't want to wait that long or to go through that.

We got pregnant again right away. We tried a different doctor this time. They immediately drew blood levels that showed that my progesterone and hCG levels were low. They gave me a progesterone shot and then an ultrasound. Again, no heartbeat was found. "Let's wait a week," they said, "it might be too early to see one." They found a heartbeat the second time, but the doctor was still "cautiously optimistic." My levels were still really low. At the third ultrasound a week later, there wasn't a heartbeat. At least this time they performed some tests to see if they could pinpoint the problem. I didn't seem to have trouble getting pregnant; I just couldn't stay pregnant. But, all the tests came back fine. Again, they weren't interested in seeing my NFP chart. Their solution was to put me on Clomid and to use over-the-counter fertility monitors to see when and if I was ovulating.

I became extremely depressed and I removed myself from the rest of the world. I didn't talk to my friends because I was afraid they would tell me that they were pregnant – again. I didn't go to the mall because I didn't want to see pregnant women. Church was even horrible because it seemed like I was surrounded by couples having babies. I became unusually bitter.

I begged my husband to try to adopt a baby. He thought I was nuts. If I could just relax, he'd say, everything would work out. I couldn't relax. I really, truly thought that I would never have any children. He agreed to go through the adoption process. It helped me to have something else to focus on, and we met other couples with infertility issues.

After six months of the Clomid, I still hadn't gotten pregnant again. Someone must have told Andrea, a good friend of mine, that we were having trouble having a baby. (Obviously, I hadn't told her. I hadn't talked with any of my friends in months.) She wrote me a letter and told me that she knew what I was feeling. She and her husband had tried for four years before they finally became pregnant. She said she owed it all to a doctor in Omaha. She knew of several other women who had been told that they'd never have children, but once they came to the Pope Paul VI Institute, they'd all had healthy babies. "Just make an appointment to let him look at your chart," she wrote. "If he doesn't feel that he can help you, he'll say so. He won't drag you through unnecessary treatments."

I prayed about it. In a novena to St. Therese of the Child Jesus,

I asked for a sign that I was doing the right thing, that things would work out and that I would be at peace with whatever happened. On the 9th day of my novena, my husband and I drove to Omaha for an appointment with Dr. Hilgers. We entered the building and took the elevator to the second floor. When the door opened, there stood a large statue of St. Therese just a few feet away. A sign? I thought so then, and now I know so.

Dr. Hilgers asked me a few questions and then asked to see my NFP chart. After a few minutes he said, "From the looks of this, I'd say you have endometriosis. To be sure, we'd need to do a series of tests and maybe even surgery." Endometriosis? Sure, I had back pain and long, drawn out periods, but I thought that everyone had that. Isn't that what Midol is for? And none of the other doctors had ever mentioned the word. But it made sense. I made appointments for a series of blood tests to monitor my hormone levels and ultrasounds at certain days of my cycle to see what was going on. I didn't understand the medical procedures or what certain blood levels meant. I believed that was what the doctor did. I trusted that God had placed me here for a reason.

Dr. Hilgers performed a diagnostic laparoscopy, which confirmed the presence of fairly extensive endometriosis as well as some deposits on my right ovary and a fibroid on my uterus. Unfortunately, because of prominent blood vessels, he was unable to safely use the laser at that time. I would need to have another surgery. My insurance company didn't agree with Dr. Hilgers. According to them, the course of treatment most accepted for my condition would be a trial of medical therapy, not surgery. We had discussed this option with Dr. Hilgers, and I even researched it a bit on my own. From everything that I had read, I had to agree with Dr. Hilgers that such medications could produce a permanent hormonal disturbance as well as bear significant side effects. We scheduled my second surgery about a month after the first. The insurance company denied coverage a day before I was scheduled to have the procedure but I had surgery anyway.

About two weeks after my surgery, we received a call from a friend who had adopted a child through the state foster care system. She knew of two children, ages 4 and 5, who were in need of a permanent home. We jumped at the chance. After waiting for so long to have a baby, we knew that we had done as much as we could to have a biological child. Who knows? Maybe this was the answer to our ever-wondering "why."

A day after we found out that the state would allow us to proceed with the foster-to-adopt process, we found out we were pregnant. We were surprised that it happened so fast but scared that we would lose the baby. Again, my hormone levels were tested and I was put on progesterone shots. I was monitored very closely and I felt that everything that could possibly be done to save this baby was being done. Those first few ultrasounds were amazing. We saw the baby's heart beat, legs kick, and even saw it hiccup! At 25 weeks we were asked to be a part of the testing of a new 3-D ultrasound machine. I had a picture of my baby's face before she was born!

Today, my husband and I have four amazing miracles. We are blessed to be the parents of two adopted children and two biological children. It was for all four of these reasons that God led us to Pope Paul VI Institute. I received care that successfully treated my endometriosis, care that enabled me to give birth to two, healthy children, and care that led me to let go and let God lead my life.

PHYSICIAN'S COMMENTS:

PREVENTION OF PRE-TERM BIRTH

Thomas W. Hilgers, M.D.

Most people are not aware that the prematurity rate (defined as the number of babies born prior to 37.0 weeks gestation) has increased consistently over the last 30 years. In 2002, the prematurity rate was 12.1 percent. In the mid-1960s, just to give you an example, the prematurity rate was only 6.7 percent.

This is a national tragedy! Premature birth is hazardous to the health of young children. Prematurity is a leading cause of cerebral palsy, mental and motor retardation, and other abnormalities. In addition, while a great deal of progress has been made in the medical care of these young infants - which is really very good - it is extremely expensive and drains the resources of an already challenged health care system.

Some of this increase is due to the large number of multiple pregnancies which have come as the result of the artificial reproductive technology programs for the treatment of infertility. Many of those programs average between 35 and 45 percent multiple pregnancy rates. This is contrasted, incidentally, with only a 3.2 percent multiple rate in **NaProTECHNOLOGY**. In addition, it is quite likely that the epidemic of sexually transmitted diseases has also had something to do with the increased risk of preterm birth in the United States.

Over the last 25 years, research has been conducted at Creighton University School of Medicine and the Pope Paul VI Institute on developing programs to reduce the prematurity rate. The Pope Paul VI Institute has developed a Prematurity Prevention Protocol (see *The Medical and Surgical Practice of* **NaProTECHNOLOGY**,

Pope Paul VI Institute Press, Omaha, NE, 2004). This Prematurity
Prevention Program has decreased the prematurity rate to 7.0
percent, and it is rare for us to see a baby born before 32.0 weeks
anymore.

This is all accomplished by educating the patient on the various symptoms of premature labor or "uterine irritability," which
is a precursor to preterm labor. These symptoms include pelvic
pressure, cramping, low backache, the uterus knotting up like a
ball, and generally not feeling well. Once patients are aware of
these symptoms, then a specific program of intervention can be
undertaken, which has been extremely successful in decreasing
the preterm delivery rate. The program involves the use of progesterone support during the course of pregnancy, medications
which help stop uterine contractions, the use of cervical cerclage
(a stitch placed in the cervix in indicated cases to strengthen the
cervix) and then the judicious use of powerful antibiotics to treat
underlying infection.

Two Full-Term Babies Achieved with Help of Institute
Colleen M. Lux

I met Dr. Hilgers when I was 39 years old, pregnant, and with a history of two stillbirths and one child who was born with a heart defect. The following is an account of my story that ended with two successful, live, full-term births, and totally healthy children.

I would like to begin with a background. My husband and I had a very hard time conceiving our first child we worked with a specialist, and after having my cervix frozen, we met with success. Our oldest son, Andrew, was born in 1983. He was born with a hole in his heart, which was successfully closed in 1985 through surgery.

Shortly after his surgery, I was amazed to find myself pregnant without any type of medical help. Unfortunately, this daughter, Kristy Jo, passed away in July of 1986. I was 26 weeks pregnant with her when we discovered that she had died inside of me. They induced me and she was delivered stillborn on July 18, 1986. An autopsy was performed, but there were no problems with Kristy, and we never were given a reason as to why she died. A few short months later I became pregnant again and this child also died inside of me during my third month, I had a D&C after discovering through an ultrasound that there were no signs of life. I then had genetic studies done, which told us that he was a genetically fine boy. Once again, we were left without any answers. After this, we went ten years without being able to conceive.

During this time of infertility, my husband's brother, who is a doctor, recommended seeing Dr. Hilgers so we could have more children. I kept his name as a reference in case I ever needed it, but chose not to actively become pregnant and open myself up to another loss. I decided that it would be up to the Lord if I ever was blessed with another baby.

A few short years later we moved to Omaha, and in less than a year, I discovered I was pregnant at the age of 39. The only doctor I would even consider going to was Dr. Hilgers. They discovered that I was extremely low on progesterone, and his associate was totally amazed that I was even pregnant due to my very scarred cervix. An ultrasound was performed, and I was definitely pregnant.

They started me on progesterone shots, and I had to continue with these throughout my pregnancy. Dr. Hilgers also added oral progesterone to supplement my low progesterone counts. I was on the most progesterone possible. I was due the latter part of April, and around Christmas I started having strange pains that were quite intense at times. I went in to the clinic after the holidays and saw Dr. Hilgers. He discovered I was in preterm labor and immediately performed a cerclage and put me to bed rest. My membranes were extremely thin, and to this day I am amazed that I was able to carry this daughter to full term. Along with the cerclage, Dr. Hilgers also put me on an IV therapy program that consisted of coming into the clinic two to three times weekly for an IV that contained antibiotics. The IV helped calm my uterus and worked miracles, as far as I'm concerned. The nurses and Dr. Hilgers were my lifeline during the next three months. My only trips out of the house consisted of going in for IVs and progesterone shots. The rest of my time was spent in bed, as when I was up, the pain was too intense, and I was doing everything possible to carry this baby full term and not lose another child.

On April 4, 1997, our daughter Claire Kathryn was born at Bergan Mercy. Dr. Hilgers induced me on that day and we welcomed our healthy, 8 pound baby into our lives. I did end up with complications from hemorrhaging and was quite ill for a couple of weeks but eventually healed.

In January of 2000, I discovered I was pregnant again! We were very surprised with this pregnancy, too, but also quite glad that Claire would have a sibling to grow up with. I ended up in preterm labor again, but we were very aware of this possibility happening. Dr. Hilgers ordered frequent ultrasounds to check my cervix, and we knew right away when it was thinning out, and I paid more attention to the pains that I was again experiencing. Once again, Dr. Hilgers performed a cerclage and put me on the same IV therapy as before. I also underwent progesterone shots and oral progesterone pills the entire pregnancy. Since we knew what to expect and look for, I did not end up on bed rest at all during this pregnancy which was a blessing. I also had frequent ultrasounds to check the baby's breathing so we would know when to have the C-section. It was amazing to see his lungs progress, and on September 29, 2000, we welcomed a 9 lb 9 oz son into our family. We named this baby Charles Otto after his great-grandfather.

As I am writing this, our children are now 20, 6, and 3 and all are a blessing. I firmly believe that without Dr. Hilgers and his wonderful staff, I would not have Claire and Charlie. They worked miracles for us!

I Couldn't Trust My Baby's Life to Anyone Else
Donesha Wilburn

I always loved children and planned to have a few of my own. It turned out that it was not as easy as it looked.

I believe my problems started with a pap smear I had in late 1995. My new OB/GYN said that my cervix was fine except for a small patch of irregular cells that should be tested further. The very painful cervical biopsy came back negative for cancer but my doctor recommended cryo-therapy to prevent the irregular cells from becoming cancerous. I had the procedure.

In a little over a month I got the best and the worst news all at the same time. The doctor told me I was pregnant and I was overjoyed. Unfortunately, the pelvic exam revealed that my baby had implanted on the inside of my cervix. Obviously, I couldn't carry a baby to term in this condition. So the same day I found out I was pregnant I found out that I wasn't going to have a baby. The next morning I had an emergency D&C. I was just 21 years old at the time.

In just a few short months I found out that I was pregnant again. It wasn't planned, but it was welcomed. As soon as I found out, I begged for an ultrasound to assure me that the baby was in the right spot. After that I was excited, but I always had a kind of uneasy feeling. According to my older sister (who was pregnant with her third baby), I was the sickest and most complaining pregnant person that she ever met. I was constantly sick; I could never keep my food down, and I quickly lost over ten pounds. I had a constant headache and there was pain in muscles I never knew I had.

Then toward the end of my third month, I started spotting. The doctor at the clinic said that like my other symptoms, this too could sometimes be normal. I looked forward to a time when I could just be pleasantly pregnant.

Then I wasn't sick as much and I started to gain weight. The spotting had stopped, and at 19 weeks I finally felt my baby move. I was on top of the world. Exactly one week after I felt my baby move, I woke up in unbelievable pain. I called the clinic and again I was told, "This is normal, put your feet up, get some rest, don't panic and call back if the pain gets worse or you start bleeding." A couple of hours later, there was still no change, but I was panicking. I needed to know why I was in pain. So I called back and insisted that someone see me today (I should have just gone straight to the ER but I didn't have insurance and couldn't afford to go without permission from my doctor). So my sister took me in at noon. I checked in with the receptionist and sat down.

Hours went by and nobody called my name even though every so often my sister waddled up to the desk and reminded them that I was in pain. It was five hours later by the time I was seen. During my exam, the doctor calmly said, "You're dilated and I want you to go to the hospital."

At the hospital I was informed that I needed a cerclage and that it was my only choice. They informed me that my bag was bulging and that I needed to lie down to take the pressure off of my cervix in the hopes that my bag would recede. I slept like that. (Well, I really didn't get much sleep). The next morning a resident introduced himself as the doctor performing the procedure. I asked a lot of questions; most of them were answered, but when I asked how many times he had performed the procedure, he got mad and told me, "Either you want the procedure or not." My mom asked the nurse, and she said that he was the only one who could do it that day and that I shouldn't wait. So, I had the procedure.

Afterwards, I was supposed to stay for observation for one day. All day I kept telling the nurse that there was fluid leaking, but she said I was imagining it because she couldn't see anything. Early the next morning I was on my way to the restroom when my water broke. I was informed that my baby would not survive, and they would do nothing to help her when she was born. They moved me to a private room. The next morning after a long and very painful labor, the nurse came in and checked to see how far I had dilated. She said, "You're at five, that might be enough, why don't you push?" So

I had my baby right there, in a regular bed, with no doctor present, and then I pushed the call button so that someone would come in and help the nurse. I left the hospital the next day with a green satin box with pictures and clothes in it, instead of my baby. I couldn't afford to have a funeral.

One of the worst things about losing a baby is that even after you accept and come to terms with your loss, you still have to explain what happened for months to people who knew you were pregnant.

A few months later, I found out I was pregnant again. I was scared of what might happen, but I tried to look forward to becoming a mother. This time I wasn't as sick, but my cervix had never really closed from the last time, so I got the cerclage early. After that, things seemed to be okay, but if you've ever had a miscarriage, you know that you just can't shake that uneasy feeling. This pregnancy seemed to be uneventful. I just prayed and waited. I waited to get big, I waited to feel him move, then I waited for my due date.

I didn't make it to my due date, however. One morning, at the beginning of my sixth month, I woke up and my bed and underwear were wet. I called the doctor's office and was told that I most likely wet the bed but just call if I started cramping. I lay on my couch with my feet up, and an hour later I noticed my clothes were wet again.

This time I didn't call, I just went to the hospital. Once I got there I was treated like I didn't know what I was talking about. The nurse did three tests, and two were positive for amniotic fluid. She said that she had to wait for the doctor to confirm the tests. I waited for hours for the doctor. Then an Obstetrician and a Pediatrician came in and told me that there was no fluid around my baby, and I would go into labor in the next 24 hours. They said my baby was too small and underdeveloped to survive. Even if he were breathing when he was born they would not help him if he weighed under one pound. They said that there was nothing they could do. So, they moved me to a different room, and I lay there feeling my son kick, waiting for labor to start. After 24 hours went by with no contractions, they began trying to induce my labor. The medicine they were using to induce labor was bad for my kidneys, so they could only give it to me for a certain amount of time each day. Three days went by without any contractions.

During this time, my family called different hospitals trying to get advice. A nurse at Bergan Mercy Hospital told my mom that in that situation, they would not just induce labor because a baby can make the amniotic fluid again, and sometimes a hole in the bag can heal itself. She also said that at their hospital they do everything they can to save the baby and the mother.

The next day, my mom wouldn't let them give me the Pitocin. My baby was still kicking and his heart rate was fine, and we knew that if I could carry him for two more weeks, his chances of survival would double. So we wanted to wait to give my baby a chance.

The staff at the hospital seemed very agitated by this and after two more days of no contractions, they informed me that if they were not treating me in some way, I had to be released from the hospital. I was told that I should stay off my feet and that inevitably I would either go into labor or an infection would set in. They told me to look for constant pain or a bright green discharge. After 24 hours at home, the pain set in. I quietly prayed for the pain to go away and never told a soul. It's hard enough to come to terms with the fact that your body has failed your baby. I knew that my family wouldn't understand. I would have borne the pain for as long as I needed if it would save him, but an infection would endanger both our lives.

So, without calling my family, I had my best friend take me to the hospital at 2:00 a.m. I was in pain but not in labor, so the staff said they didn't know how to help me. They wanted to send me home but I insisted that they keep me because of the infection. They only agreed to give me pain medicine to help me sleep and said we would talk again in a few hours. However, in a few hours there was no need for discussion; I was in labor. The pain of labor was increased by the pain of the infection. They gave me an epidural, but it only worked on half my body. Later that afternoon, I gave birth to a beautiful baby boy. He didn't cry, but he was breathing. I held him only for a few minutes before I was rushed off to surgery to stop my hemorrhaging. When I returned, he was gone. My sister placed his lifeless body in my arms. A couple of days later I left my son at the hospital. Again, returning home with a green satin box instead of my baby.

I never wanted to try to get pregnant again. But, a little over a year later, I found out I was again with child. I was horrified, but my sister knew someone who had to have a cerclage and be on bedrest, so she called her to find out who her doctor was. That's how I met the doctors and nurses at the Pope Paul VI Institute. They got me into the office as soon as possible. I think I was about two and a half months along. I was schedule for an ultrasound right away. It showed that my cervix was already open and I needed a cerclage right away.

I loved the staff and I got to know them well. I was always in the office. They checked things like my hormone levels and my probability for infections on a regular basis. I got hormone shots and IV antibiotics. I also had frequent ultrasounds. Then I was put on bedrest and they set up a home health nurse to come and administer my medications and keep track of my growth and weight gain. In the end, I had a minor complication that caused me to have a C-Section, but what a small price for such a wonderful gift – my son. I named him Nathaniel, which means "a gift from God."

I now have two beautiful little boys. Dr. Hilgers again took care of my pregnancy with Carlos. I believe that due to the wonderful care that I received with my first son, my body was a lot stronger the second time around. I still had to get hormone shots and IV antibiotics, but I didn't have to get my cerclage until I was five months pregnant, and I was only on moderate bedrest.

If I could, I would have all my friends and family get their prenatal care at Pope Paul VI Institute. I know that if I ever get pregnant again, Dr. Hilgers will be the first person I call. I couldn't trust my baby's life to anyone else.

My Arms are Anything but Empty Now
Annette Hollister

On Valentine's Day in 1993, I was in the Neonatal Intensive Care Unit, holding my tiny baby with my hand on his chest, hoping to feel a heartbeat. After two months of strict bed rest and even stays in the hospital, hoping to stave off birth, Joshua Edward was born on February 13th after only 25 weeks gestation – almost three months early. I had been told that he would not live through the night, and yet his life signs were stable the next morning. However, at a pound and half and barely the length of a ruler, his health took a rapid turn for the worse. I was able to hold him for the first time, cradling him among the wires and tubes. I did not want to believe the alarms on the monitors, but then a doctor confirmed that my baby was no longer with us. Grief washed over me like a typhoon.

Unfortunately, the grieving process was placed on hold as I was still fighting for my own life. Within a week after delivering and the day after my baby's funeral, I began to pass large blood clots and bleed heavily. Although I was rushed to the hospital on more than one occasion for this condition during the next several weeks, it was not until I was six weeks postpartum that a D&C was performed. An examination of the contents removed by the D&C confirmed that small pieces of the placenta were retained inside my uterus from the delivery. Although it was admitted that no one understood the reasons for his premature birth, one of the doctors from the team treating me (while pregnant and postpartum) speculated that perhaps the cause of my son's premature birth was a disintegrating placenta from some unknown cause.

Unfortunately, the D&C was not to be the end of my visits to the hospital. In fact, I began another ordeal with hemorrhaging on and off. At one point I was referred to an endocrinologist who placed me on birth control pills in the hopes of controlling the bleeding.

This was not successful. The next step was to give me injections of the hormone, Lupron, which placed me in a state of medical menopause. Although I was only 22 years old, I experienced night sweats, hot flashes and thinning hair. Oh yes, and after several injections, the bleeding did finally stop, and I was without periods for months to come. This was a grateful relief in more ways than one as I had been advised that if the drug was not effective, my uterus would need to be removed.

It was under the threat of a hysterectomy that I sought opinions from other physicians and found myself at the Pope Paul VI Institute with a new doctor and a new hope for my life. I was treated for the next few years to adjust the severe hormone imbalance presumably left over from previous treatments. Although it appeared after a time that I had been given the "green light" to try again for another baby, the pain from past experience was so great and the fear of losing another baby was so strong that it would be almost eight years until my husband and I tried again.

We had been using the **CREIGHTON MODEL FertilityCare™ System** to avoid pregnancy through those years and now we used it to achieve pregnancy. To our delight, the method was effective for us and I was pregnant very soon after trying. Unfortunately, our hearts were again broken when I miscarried. A few months afterward, it was discovered that I had endometriosis that had spread outside the uterus, and surgery was performed to remove as much as was possible at that time.

After the physical healing process, the longing for a baby was powerful and my arms felt so empty.My husband shared both my desire for children as well as the pain of disappointment.

This time, trying to get pregnant was not as easy, and after almost a year of trying, I thought something must be wrong with me. Thinking that the encounter with endometriosis was a factor, I scheduled exploratory surgery, only to learn five days prior to surgery that I was pregnant. Elation and shock moved me to tears – but what of this baby's future?

Right away I received progesterone injections and my hormone levels were closely monitored. As further precaution, I also received ultrasounds within the first few months to monitor and confirm the condition of the precious cargo my body held, as well as the parts holding it. The pregnancy progressed without problem until around 20 weeks gestation when I began to spot and cramp. Panic and fear gripped my heart that I might lose yet another baby. Once again I was placed on bed rest, which I was all too familiar with from my first pregnancy. However, I also was prescribed the drug, Terbutaline, in order to control the cramping of my uterus. In addition, my blood levels were monitored closely for something called High Sensitivity C-Reactive Protein (HSCRP) which indicates any level of infection in the body. Mine was elevated, so a treatment radical to my thinking was introduced – intravenous administration of antibiotics three days a week. Much to my relief, bed rest lasted only a few days. The progesterone and Terbutaline continued until 37 weeks gestation, and the IVs continued until almost 40 weeks, but were reduced to two days a week for the last few weeks. I had reached the goal of carrying the pregnancy to term. In fact, you could say that it was so successful that I had to be induced a few days before my baby's due date. This was necessary since it turned out that Nora Marie was a very robust newborn at almost 11 pounds (10 pounds 15 ½ ounces to be exact!) born on February 9, 2002.

When Nora was 11 months old, we learned that she was going to be a big sister. I once again followed the routine of progesterone monitoring and injections. Then around 20 weeks of gestation, a familiar problem surfaced…I began to feel cramping. Spotting had not yet occurred, however Dr. Hilgers acted swiftly and prescribed Terbutaline, as well as again monitoring my HSCRP levels. Within a few weeks, the elevation of my levels became of more concern and I once again started the IV treatments. This time instead of two or three times a week until the pregnancy was considered full-term, I followed a regime of IVs ten days in a row, which took approximately one hour to administer each day.

To my amazement, I never had the need to be placed on bed rest, and no further IV treatments were required for the remainder of this pregnancy. I was doing things that I never thought were possible with my previous pregnancies such as packing and moving to another state for my husband's job and chasing a toddler. Admittedly, I was feeling so confident that this pregnancy was out of the danger zone that I decided to discontinue use of the Terbutaline at 35 weeks gestation and the progesterone at 36 weeks.

Then at almost 39 weeks, due to concern of a large baby, I was induced. On September 26, 2003, our new daughter, Brynn Evelyn, entered the world at 8 pounds 7 ounces (Brynn is a Celtic name meaning "small hill," which we felt appropriate since she was not nearly as large as her sister at birth).

Although the days of deep grieving for my first child are past, I will never forget Joshua. I also can't help but wonder and be saddened at the thought that my little boy might still be with us today had the doctors at the time been aware of the benefits of progesterone and IV antibiotic treatments.

I am unsure if I will be blessed with more children in the future. For now, with a toddler and a new baby, my arms are anything but empty these days. I am pleased to say that the girls fill our lives with challenges, amazement, laughter and joy every day.

Our Miracle Baby After Tubal Reversal
Karla Nauert

I don't remember the dates exactly, but between the end of 1987 and the spring of 1988, I had three miscarriages. And let me tell you what an awful feeling. A part of you literally dies in more ways than one. After the third miscarriage, Dr. Miller, my local physician said, "We need to send you to a specialist." He then called the Gynecologists in Hastings, Nebraska, who declined to take me as a patient, because of the difficulties.

That is when he turned to Dr. Thomas Hilgers. I believe it was sometime in May of 1988 I was under Dr Hilgers's care. I became pregnant shortly after. Believe me, I was scared. I cried a lot and prayed a lot. I was started immediately on hCG and progesterone shots. I ran into one difficulty after another. There was bleeding, bed rest and lots of worrying.

At 24 weeks into my pregnancy my amniotic fluid was slowly leaking, and I was having contractions. I was put in the hospital in Hastings but sent to Omaha to be under Dr Hilgers's care. They were able to stop labor with oral medication and I was sent home to be on total bed rest. I could only get up to go to the restroom. I had a three year old daughter (Kara Kay) who still had to go to daycare; I had meals delivered to me for lunch. We had to live off of my husband's salary, because, of course, I had to stop working and ran out of maternity leave.

But, one week later I started bleeding pretty badly and having more contractions. The oral medication stopped working. So, back to Mary Lanning Hospital and then to Omaha again. This time it was for a while. I was put in a small room with no windows, because they wanted me to be close to the Neonatal Intensive Care Unit. The doctors were giving all kinds of different drugs to stop labor. And talk about IVs - boy I had a lot of them. And blood was drawn from me all the time. They also had to give me four pints of blood. That was scary.

Now, I wasn't just totally bed-ridden, I was totally bed-ridden in the hospital in Omaha, a two hour drive from my husband and daughter, whom I only got to see on the weekends. They didn't even like to come to see me because it was hard for them to leave and everyone would cry. I was so depressed. But, we also knew what we were doing was for the baby.

The nurses and doctors were so good to me. For Thanksgiving one of the doctors brought me a home cooked meal. My family couldn't come up for the holiday. And for my birthday, which was in November, the nurses decorated my room for me. They would give me back rubs, comfort me when I cried. They also brought me magazines, cross-stitching and chocolate. Dr Hilgers also brought me some chocolate shakes with bananas. They were all so wonderful. But, their whole goal was to get me to 40 weeks, so I had 16 weeks to go.

But, after all the drugs and everything they tried, the time had really come, and everything they tried wasn't good enough. Our baby boy, Jeremy Michael, was born 6 weeks later at 30 weeks, weighing 3 lbs. 2½ oz; bigger than they expected. But, he was rushed to the Neonatal Intensive Care Unit. He was given two doses of Surfactant, which at that time was experimental. But, with all the support from everyone and God, our little boy did pretty well. I believe he had to be in the hospital for eight weeks or so. Every weekend we made a trip to Omaha to visit our little guy. We called every day to check on him.

That year we spent Christmas at Bergan Mercy Hospital. He was flown back to Hastings to spend the last couple of weeks in the hospital closer to his family. But, he had only been home about two months when he caught a terrible viral pneumonia and was flown back to Omaha Children's Hospital for about a four week stay. Even with steady medication he had a tremendous number of pneumonia episodes, two bouts of RSV and he was on a heart monitor until he was ten months old. After he was off of the heart monitor, they told us they thought Jeremy had an infected piece in his right lung that might be causing some of the problems. There were no guarantees.

We went ahead and had the surgery done at the Children's Hospital in Omaha. It was really hard to hand our baby over for surgery. But, I really think it helped. He still would get sick, but not nearly as bad, and now he is 15 years old and is doing really well. He has an infection once in awhile but, nothing like it was before the surgery. I had a pretty healthy baby, considering, but I was so depressed and didn't want to go through that again. It's not just emotions; finances are a real stressful part of all of this. Just Jeremy's hospital and doctor bills were somewhere around $250,000 by the time he was two years old, and that didn't include my bills. Thank goodness we had really good insurance through our work. But, with all of that, I decided to have my tubes tied.

Later, on in life, I remarried, and my husband, Brian, didn't have any children, and we wanted one. So, back to Dr Hilgers. My fears were still there. I didn't forget any of what I went through nine years earlier. Dr Hilgers did the surgery, but no guarantees. My tubes were repaired; Dr Hilgers said they were pretty short and the right one almost didn't have enough to be repaired.

But, we were on our way only to run into a lot of hardships. First, we ended up having two miscarriages. Dr. Hilgers thought possibly they were in the tube to begin with, so we decided to have the right tube and ovary removed. When that was done, we discovered it was much harder to conceive than we thought. I was on some hormone medicines, but nothing happened. So, we gave up and decided that was the way it was supposed to be.

And, then I told my husband that I thought I was pregnant, so we took in a urine sample. Dr. Miller's nurse called and said, "You're pregnant." I then called my husband to tell him, and he had no idea I even went in. He was excited but told me not to get my hopes up. Too late but, I knew why he was telling me that.

We had a long haul ahead of us. We got a hold of Dr Hilgers, who immediately started me on hCG and progesterone shots. OUCH! (It's really not that bad). Dr Hilgers decided to put a stitch in my cervix to hopefully help me from miscarrying. After the surgery, I felt somewhat relieved, but still scared, real scared.

Later in the pregnancy, Dr Hilgers put me on some antibiotic IVs, just in case an infection is what threw me into labor the last time.

After, months of some bed rest, a little bleeding and a lot of shots and worrying, the time was getting closer for the doctors to take the stitch out of my cervix. It was removed at 37 weeks and exactly a week later, I had my little baby boy (Austin Scott). He weighed 6 lbs. 3 oz. My husband was overwhelmed. We were all so excited that Austin was doing so well. He has some minor health issues, but over all, he is doing great.

I never really got to enjoy being pregnant because I was worrying about what was going to happen next. But, I'm so thankful to have my boys. They are true miracles; every baby is.

PHYSICIAN'S COMMENTS:

PREMENSTRUAL SYNDROME (PMS)

Thomas W. Hilgers, M.D.

It is not easy to determine the number of women who suffer from a series of symptoms that regularly recur during the premenstrual phase of their menstrual cycle. However, it is thought that this represents a very large group. The symptoms include irritability, breast tenderness, bloating, weight gain, carbohydrate craving, teariness, depression, headache, fatigue and insomnia. If these symptoms begin four or more days prior to the onset of menstruation (and the usual is seven to ten days), then it is called either Premenstrual Syndrome or Premenstrual Dysphoric Disorder. This condition can be very severe, causing a great deal of suffering, for not only the woman, but also for her spouse and children.

These symptoms, however, can be treated and treated very effectively. The **CREIGHTON MODEL Fertility***Care*™ **System** and the new women's health science of **NaProTECHNOLOGY** have taught us how to measure certain hormones during the course of the menstrual cycle. This targets the cycle to the appropriate time that the hormone, when measured, will be determined to be either normal or abnormal. As everyone knows, the hormones of the menstrual cycle are not the same from one day to the next. Thus, one of the keys in **NaProTECHNOLOGY** investigation is to be able to target the menstrual cycle properly. This can easily be done in a woman who charts her menstrual cycles using the **CREIGHTON MODEL System**, and reproducible results in the monitoring of their hormones can be carried out. In this fashion, a definitive diagnosis of abnormal hormone production can be made.

Once that diagnosis is made, then a program of treatment can be implemented, which is also used in a way which properly targets the cycle. The most common treatment used now at the Pope Paul VI Institute is a hormone called Human Chorionic Gonadotropin (hCG). This treatment is given during the post-ovulatory phase of the menstrual cycle. It stimulates the production of both progesterone and estrogen from the ovary during that phase of the menstrual cycle, correcting the underlying hormonal dysfunction.

In addition, there is a hormone called Beta-Endorphin, which has also been shown to be decreased in these women. A medicine called Naltrexone has been shown to be very helpful in this group of patients.

The overall success rate of the Pope Paul VI Institute's treatment program for Premenstrual Syndrome is in the 85 to 95 percent range. In some cases, it is almost miraculous as to the type of recovery that women experience.

The Question that Changed My Life
Deborah M. Brock

Why is it so dark outside? Why is the sun shining on this beautiful Spring day but I feel no joy? What is happening to me? Am I going crazy? It didn't used to be this way.

I should have known from the beginning that something was wrong with the way my ovaries were functioning. Right after I got married in 1981, I immediately miscarried twice. Then my first child, Matthew, was born in 1983. In 1984, during my fourth pregnancy, I bled profusely. The clots were calf liver sized, but by God's grace, I carried to term a little girl, Colleen.

I had no bleeding during pregnancy with my third child, Jillian, in 1986, but experienced placenta acreta after her birth (the placenta didn't deliver.) In 1988, I bled so much during the first trimester with Mary Kate I needed to wear diapers. Again, our baby made it.

All this time no doctor diagnosed or ever tested for low progesterone, which could have been the cause of the bleeding. Even having a Bachelors of Science degree in Nursing didn't give me enough information to learn that I had an ovarian dysfunction and how to prevent these miscarriages. I miscarried again in 1989. All that the doctors would say is that "it happens sometimes."

In 1990, my daughter, Anne, was born. After each of the births, the nurses would comment about how unhealthy the placenta looked. That should have been a clue to me and them that I was having a problem with low progesterone. But again, all of the symptoms went over our heads, as we weren't educated enough to know differently.

In 1991, my sixth child, Bernadette, was born, but again the placenta wouldn't come out. As a consequence, I bled profusely. The nurses and doctors rushed to start more I.V.s and get me to the O.R. for a D&C as my blood pressure dropped precipitously low. I needed two units of blood to bring me back to normal.

In 1993, our beloved son, Joseph, was born. I had no bleeding during that pregnancy, but we had the sorrow of his death from SIDS at two and a half months of age.

A year later God blessed us with Maureen, our eighth live birth. Two years later at the age of 39, I was experiencing my 12th pregnancy. At 20 weeks the doctor found no heartbeat. An ultrasound revealed the baby had died. This really shocked me. All my other miscarriages were at six to eight weeks, so this one was very difficult to bear. My husband flew home from a business trip. We had Mary Agnes buried near Joseph at a local Catholic cemetery.

In 1997, at the age of 40, some girlfriends and I were at a local park discussing our prenatal histories and how our fertility signs were changing with age. One friend, Catherine, was an R.N. who had been trained by Dr. Hilgers at the Pope Paul VI Institute. I commented to her about the brown spotting I was starting to have prior to my period. She said, "Oh, that may be a sign of low progesterone. Perhaps that's why your baby (Mary Agnes) died in the mid-trimester. You should check it out."

I immediately went home and called the Institute, and they ordered a series of blood tests to see what the problem could be. The lab values showed an ovarian dysfunction that was causing low progesterone levels. I asked, "Is there anything I can do to prevent miscarrying in the future?" I was informed that all that was needed was to monitor my blood and be put on an hCG regimen prior to conception and hCG and progesterone after conception to keep the placenta healthy so it can nourish and support the young life.

When I got off the phone I remember crying and crying, grieving over all the miscarried babies that perhaps could have been brought to term had I known this before. Along with the grief, I was really angry at the doctors who told me there was nothing that could be done to prevent a miscarriage. I found it incredible that in all my years of nursing training I never heard anything that could have helped me see that some miscarriages can be prevented.

I immediately became one of Dr. Hilgers's out-of-state patients. Our 13th baby was conceived and for the first trimester, I was mailing blood samples every other week and taking hCG and progesterone shots twice a week. Our miracle child was born the day after my 41st birthday on the Feast of Our Mother of Sorrows. We named her Maria. I have a great devotion to Our Mother under that title because she helped me through all the losses of our children.

After Maria's birth in 1998, something new started to happen. I became depressed. "Oh well," I thought, "I have eight living children fifteen and under. No wonder I'm overwhelmed. I'm homeschooling the children and this is simply getting too hard. I was born in sunny southern California and now I'm stuck in a Midwest winter. Of course I'm depressed. This will pass."

But it didn't. As the months went on over the course of the next three years, I became more and more depressed. Even though I knew I had insufficient hormones to be able to carry a baby to term without hormonal support, I was unaware that low hormones can also cause serious depression.

Over time I felt I couldn't cope with the children; my joy had turned to a burden. I thought it was because of home schooling or the frequent moves of our household or because of the occasional teen attitudes I was dealing with. I rarely shared my internal struggle with others. Only my dear husband and two friends, Katy and Terry, were aware of all the dark feelings I was having and supported me through the tough time. I had a flat affect. I had a passive death wish. I wanted to die, I felt so miserable. But because of my strong faith, I would never do anything about that wish. I felt disconnected from my body at times. I didn't feel as capable as I once did of taking on apostolic projects for the Church. I wanted to hide from my kids. I would often rock in my chair in my room alone with my door shut nursing my baby, staring out at God's beautiful creation and feeling nothing but misery; flat, dark, tired. I felt I was sputtering along on mere fumes with no gas in my tank.

In 2001, at the age of 44, we decided to have some hormonal blood tests to evaluate what my fertility picture was like in this perimenopausal state. I contacted Dr. Hilgers at the Pope Paul VI Institute once again. The nurse called to let me know that my hormone values were low. Very low. So low in fact that I had only one third of the normal estrogen and progesterone for a woman my age.

Then the nurse asked one of the most important questions that had ever been asked of me in my life. In fact, a question that eventually changed my life for the better! "Debbie, your hormones are so very low. Are you ever depressed?" I couldn't believe my ears. "Yes! I am depressed," I answered. "I'm very depressed. It started three years ago and has gotten progressively worse." I felt that I was coming out of the dark to even admit that. Who admits to being depressed? Obviously, something was wrong with me. But, I thought it was my mind, my psyche; not my body! Never in my wildest dreams, even as a nurse, with my history of low progesterone and repeated miscarriages did I think my depression was biological in origin. "Can it be cured?" I asked. "Yes! We put many women on hCG and they feel better after the second shot." the nurse answered.

I couldn't believe my ears! That month I was placed on hCG on Peak Day +3, +5, +7, and +9. Four injections every month, which my husband or I administer. These shots have helped my ovaries produce appropriate levels of estrogen and progesterone.

My depression disappeared immediately and has not returned. I am now 46 years old. I can laugh again. The children are my joy. My husband said he saw a mask lifted from my face. I love this life!

I went to the staff at Pope Paul VI Institute three years ago trying to find out about my fertility. Because of the awesome expertise of the nurses, they had the knowledge to ask the million dollar question that helped me learn about and leave hormonal depression.

Another confirmation of the physiological basis of my depression came to me over a year ago when we were in the process of a move. Due to the hectic time, I missed my medication. The symptoms of depression came flooding back. They disappeared again the next month when I got back on my hCG regimen.

God allowed me to go through the dark days of hormonal depression and find hope in treatment. Now I have been able to help others. When women come to me complaining of depression, I tell them to get a baseline medical exam to evaluate their hormone levels before they assume their depression is only in their minds.

The Institute and Dr. Hilgers and staff have helped and will help innumerable women. I, for my part, owe a debt of gratitude to them for the healthy birth of my youngest daughter, Maria, and my deliverance from a serious hormonal depression to a life of joy.

I Am Amazed at How Different I Feel
Martha Krings

For most of my life I have had to struggle with Premenstrual Syndrome. I thought this was normal and everyone went through this. For me, the symptoms were primarily irritability, fatigue, feeling down and crying easily.

In recent years, I noticed these symptoms increasing. In particular, a few days before my cycle would start, I would feel like something dropped inside me. I would be fine one day and then the next day I would be down and very tired. This would last until my cycle started. Once it started, I would feel good until next month. I started noticing this happening about the same time each month and began thinking something must be different about my system. My hormones must be dropping lower than normal. I asked my doctor about it, but he did not have any recommendations. So, I thought this was how I was made and I would have to learn to deal with it each month.

Then my sister told me that a friend had told her that Dr. Thomas Hilgers at the Pope Paul VI Institute treats women with low progesterone. When I heard about this, I knew I needed to be checked out, so I made an appointment to see him.

I learned to chart my cycles with the **CREIGHTON MODEL Fertility***Care*™ **System**. Then with the use of that charting, the blood tests showed that on a particular day of my cycle, my progesterone dropped lower than normal and stayed low until the end of the cycle.

I was started on progesterone injection shots. I receive these shots on the Peak +3, 5, 7, 9 and 11th day of my cycle. I have been receiving these shots for almost two years now and I am amazed at

189

the difference in how I feel. I am much calmer and the fatigue and depression symptoms have significantly decreased. There are some months when I feel so good I do not realize my cycle is about to start. I only know by my chart.

In addition, Dr. Hilgers also looked at other aspects of my health. I found out my thyroid and beta-endorphins were low. I have been receiving treatment for these, and I feel like a different person. I am able to handle the stresses of life so much better.

Charting is Tool in Evaluation and Treatment of PMS
Susan Loughnane

My name is Susan Loughnane and I am a practitioner for the **CREIGHTON MODEL FertilityCare™ System**. I am also a patient of Dr. Thomas Hilgers and have been on a treatment protocol for PMS (Premenstrual Syndrome) for about six years. PMS was a significant problem in my life for many years, and this article will share with you my experiences of seeking and undergoing treatment with **NaProTECHNOLOGY**.

My husband, Steve, and I have been married for 17 years. We have three children, ages 15, 13 and 9. We didn't come to know natural family planning until after our second child was born but that's another story. Our Introductory Session to the **CREIGHTON MODEL** was in early March, 1993 at a Catholic hospital in South Carolina, where my husband was stationed at the time. I remember walking out of the session in amazement because here I was, a mother of two, and I learned more about my body and the way the hormones function in that one session than I had ever known before. Our practitioner was Teresa Shelley, and she did question me about PMS on more than one occasion. She had given me a copy of the information on the treatment of PMS from the Medical Applications of Natural Family Planning book and had explained how **NaProTECHNOLOGY** could help me. ✐

I listened and read the information but still had the mindset that I could deal with this on my own. I had always experienced some form of PMS and recall distinct periods in high school and college when it seemed particularly severe. I had many emotional and physical symptoms that occurred regularly seven to ten days prior to my period. This included (but was not limited too) irritability, mood swings, crying spells, depressed type feelings, as well as bloating, breast tenderness, backache, carbohydrate craving, and hypoglycemic symptoms. The one to two days prior to my period, I would literally hate the world and everyone in it! After I was married and started to have children, I noticed that the PMS symptoms appeared to intensify after each birth. I did experience some mild to moderate postpartum depression after each of my children's births, but I thought I could handle it and never sought treatment.

In early 1994, we were now living in Pennsylvania and wanted to have another child. My third pregnancy was more difficult, in fact, I was sick almost the entire pregnancy. I couldn't ride in a car without getting motion sickness. The fifth month was the only month that I felt reasonably good. Our youngest child, Matthew, was born on December 29, 1994. I had constant and overwhelming fatigue after his birth and was extremely emotional. Nursing him actually seemed to calm me down, probably due to the oxytocin kicking in. My cycles returned when Matt was 14 months old, and I remember thinking, if this is what PMS was going to be like, it was going to be a rough road. Stress levels were high – we had moved from Pennsylvania to Virginia when Matt was only six months old.

After a family vacation in the summer of 1996, I became ill and seemed to have a difficult time recovering. I was having stomach/intestinal related ailments with periods of abdominal pain. At the same time, I was weaning Matt and I began to experience night sweats, nausea, sensitivity to cold, and episodes of heart racing in addition to the fatigue and other symptoms. I became somewhat of a human guinea pig as I visited doctors, trying to find relief from PMS and my stomach problems. My family practice doctor thought I was just anxious (which I was) and prescribed Ativan (a tranquilizer) and eventually Buspar since the Ativan knocked me out and I was afraid to take it. She put me on Prilosec to treat the GERD (Gastro Reflux Disease) she thought I had and referred me to a gastroenterologist. He gave me medication for Giardia which made me extremely ill. One of the Army doctors, an internist I was referred to, was convinced that it was my gall bladder causing my problems and gave me medication for that. Everyone seemed to think I had a thyroid problem, but every time my thyroid levels were tested, they were within normal range. I hit a real low point when I went to one of the best endocrinologists in Virginia, and he handed me the name of a psychologist because he thought that was what I needed. He had not looked at my medical history or summary. As for the Creighton Model charts I had brought with me, he thought they looked nice but admitted that he didn't know much about that area. He didn't think PMS was an issue.

When I was placed on the gall bladder medicine mentioned above, I had to stop nursing totally. Three days after stopping nursing, I felt my emotions plunge and went into more severe depressed symptoms. This, unfortunately, coincided with the return of monster PMS symptoms. My OB/GYN doctor said she had read about some cases of delayed postpartum depression when the woman either stops nursing or when her cycles return and wondered if this had happened in my case. I began to have trouble sleeping and experienced panic, anxiety attacks, and dizziness in addition to the depression. Physically, I would feel absolutely horrible about four to five days prior to my period. I would actually have blackout spells, which scared me since I was trying to care for a baby and two other children. I lost about 25 to 30 pounds during this time and was a mess!

My father-in-law drove my mother-in-law down from Pennsylvania three different times to help me care for the children. I will never forget their generosity at a time when we really needed the help. In an effort to remedy the stomach ailments, I tried to eat as healthy as possible (which I thought would help with the PMS). I walked daily and eventually began taking T'ai Chi classes at a local YMCA. I cut back on sugar, eliminated caffeine, etc. ... but couldn't get a handle on the PMS completely.

I contacted my original NFP practitioner and she gave me the information to submit a referral letter and packet to the Pope Paul VI Institute. She also referred me to another NFP practitioner who had been treated for PMS by Dr. Hilgers. This "angel" provided me with guidance and talked me through many of my worst days. She truly went above and beyond the call of Christian charity.

I submitted a referral letter to Dr. Hilgers at the Institute and within a few weeks, I received a response. He was interested in looking more closely at progesterone and other hormone levels. I did notice at this time that my charting pattern had changed with the post-Peak phases becoming shorter. The starting point was the hormonal evaluation. I found a lab manager at a hospital 45 minutes away who was willing to assist me with the evaluation. When the results were analyzed and I contacted the nurses at the Institute, I literally sobbed on the phone. My levels of estradiol, progesterone, DHEA and Beta-endorphins were very low. (I personally like to use the term rock bottom.) I had tried to convince myself that I was either crazy or anxious and that I could make this go away somehow. The nurse explained that this was a medical condition that could be treated, and we began to do so. I started with Naltrexone in smaller dosages and currently take 8 mg., 4 times per day. The intramuscular injections of hCG were started as well as a combination of other medications. In the beginning, a nurse friend gave me the shots, but my husband learned how to do it and is quite proficient at it. Added to the protocol was DHEA. Over the years, my treatment protocol has been refined to include estradiol (post-Peak), oral progesterone (we tried the cream initially), and for awhile, I was also taking Vitex (a women's herbal supplement). The changes began to occur gradually, but the hCG injections tended to have a more immediate effect. My husband and I are still amazed at the effect that this treatment has had on my cycles and my life!

Ironically, the stomach issues appear to have been related to a stomach bacteria called H. Pylori. I had been misdiagnosed for months. When I had to switch doctors due to insurance, my new doctor tested me for it almost immediately. I was treated with antibiotics and Prilosec, and after three days of treatment, my appetite returned and food tasted good again.

Many people thought I was crazy – trusting some doctor in Nebraska who had never even seen me. I believed he was a man of integrity and I believed he had great respect for women. I had researched different approaches to PMS treatment before contacting him. I totally put my trust in God during this time and He led me in the direction of the Pope Paul VI Institute. I began the treatment in November, 1996 and my quality of life improved gradually over time. I also read a lot of inspirational books, engaged in prayer and Bible study, meditation and exercise, as well as trying to surround myself with positive people. I had to also look at such issues as stress management. My personality is such that I tend to be perfectionistic, analytical, etc., qualities that can sometimes make one more prone to anxiety type disorders. I did a number of self-help measures to help with some of the cognitive aspects of recovery. When I started to feel good again, I couldn't imagine why I had waited so long to pursue treatment. It has made a difference in how I interact with my family. I think I have become a better parent because I'm not experiencing the Jekyll and Hyde transformations every month.

Well, I think that God had a plan all along for me to be teaching the **CREIGHTON MODEL**. During my recovery, I began to think about the possibility of teaching someday. Having gone through this experience has made me more empathetic and sensitive to other women who are experiencing severe PMS. I really wanted to be able to assist women with charting and getting help with all types of reproductive issues. My family and I eventually returned home to Pennsylvania in October, 1997, and we live outside the Pittsburgh area. I happened to see an article in the Pittsburgh Catholic on NFP with a photo of Dr. Paul M. Hoover and his family. Dr. Hoover is a Creighton Medical Consultant. He and his wife, Patti, in conjunction with Fr. Ronald Lawler and Fr. Kris Stubna, brought Kathy Rivet and her training program to Pittsburgh. Shirley Hoefler was the other educator who took part in this process. I began Education Phase I on February 12, 2000 and took my final exam on February 17, 2001 and passed! I became a knowledge addict – reading books, listening to audiotapes – any material I could get my hands on to increase my understanding of the Church's teaching, NFP and **NaProTECHNOL-OGY**. My husband's support has been a solid force throughout this learning and discernment process.

My message to all women is to be informed and empowered. Learn to respect and appreciate your fertility with the **CREIGHTON MODEL Fertility*Care*™ System**. Have hope that **NaProTECHNOLOGY** will continue to provide answers for reproductive issues that you may deal with in your lifetime. The charting is an excellent medical record and can be a valuable tool in the evaluation and treatment of PMS, among other things.

My journey was one from a contraceptive user to the **CREIGHTON MODEL** user to Practitioner! All things are truly possible for God.

From Death to New Life
Michaela Blazek

I've suffered with premenstrual syndrome (PMS) as far back as the late 1970s. I was in my early 20s and newly married. It has not only affected the quality of my life, but my family's as well. PMS was just a joke back then among husbands and talk show hosts. In fact, the syndrome had just been given a name to describe "that crazy time of the month." It was normal for all women to have some PMS, but as the years went by, I felt anything but normal. The symptoms that used to last one to five days before my period were lasting two to three weeks. I lived with a dull headache much of the time. I spent many years treating symptoms, until one night in prayer, I asked God to help me. That is when things began to change.

I was 33 years old when I was going to have my last child, or so I thought. The plan was to have a tubal ligation after my last C-section. We didn't do it, for no other reason than we just didn't get it scheduled. My OB/GYN at the time, a kind and caring man, who delivered my three beautiful daughters, kept asking the same question every year. What are you doing for birth control? I had taken the birth control pill for a year and a half after I was married, but due to severe migraines, I stopped. I then used a series of different methods other than the IUD, since it was an abortifacient. I would never do that, I told myself. Little did I know then that the pill had the same potential. I now believe that it was the grace of God that kept me from continuing on the pill or going through with the tubal ligation. Having said that, I do not in any way judge those who have. There was not the research and information back then that there is now. Besides, our generation does like to be in control, hence the term, birth control. We would try to have and do it all, in our own way, and on our own timeline. They say if you want to make God laugh, make plans!

Life was going at warp speed with careers, growing children and volunteering here and there. We were a church-going family, and I loved my family, parish and friends. Life was quite good until my mother became ill. She died of congestive heart failure within six months of a rare diagnosis. Life was changed forever. Life was precious, and somehow making sure I saw my mother again someday was of the utmost importance. I was grief stricken and tired.

When I saw my doctor again that year, the same question regarding my fertility persisted and I suddenly - without knowing where it came from - said I wanted to try natural family planning. He was neither negative nor positive on it, but said he hoped it worked. They gave no information at the office, and I left just knowing I needed to pursue something to which I'd never given a second thought. Birth control was a fuzzy, gray area back in the 1970s and we just accepted that we could "follow our own conscience." I now know where that prompting to try NFP came from. It was the Holy Spirit, and I have since learned to listen much more carefully when making important decisions in my life.

We don't blame anyone for our decision to use birth control. My husband and I could have educated ourselves on this Catholic teaching, but instead we did what many others were doing. The pill was popular and easy. We have paid a price for such ease. My health had been deteriorating over the years. I was more and more tired, telling myself it was one more child, the stress of my mother's death, too many commitments, etc. etc. The migraines persisted, and I was sent to a neurologist. The medication they put me on worked, but it would knock me out for a day or two, interrupting my life, my children's lives, and my husband's life. In the meantime, I had learned to chart my cycles. I had not connected what was being charted to my deteriorating health. Here I was a nurse, and in such denial! Finally, after three months the FertilityCare instructor said to me, "Do you have a lot of PMS?" The light bulb went on. "Well, I do have migraines, fatigue, mood swings, and my husband sure thinks so!" She thought I most likely had a low progesterone level, and possibly some other hormonal imbalances. I should see someone and get that straightened out. But who, I thought. My regular OB/GYN would not know how to read these charts, and I did not want to be put back on the pill. I decided to leave it in God's hands and scheduled an appointment at the Pope Paul VI Institute where I had learned to chart. It was a good decision too, because four months after my mother's death, I was pregnant. With a busy husband, not feeling well, and not keeping up with our charting, we were given a surprise. Difficult at first, to adjust to the idea of being 38 years old and pregnant again, we were soon very excited. I knew then why I did not have the tubal ligation, and I felt God had given us a new life to ease the loss of my mother. The circle of life continued, but we were soon to experience more heartache.

I got right into my doctor at the Institute, another kind and caring man, and was told my blood work was not normal. You see, I had not been in to get that hormonal imbalance straightened out yet. My progesterone and estrogen levels and several other levels were very low. They would start me on hCG shots right away and try to get those levels to where they needed to be to sustain a pregnancy. I was feeling so good, though, that I was sure there would not be a problem. I was wrong. At 14 weeks, I lost "Timothy," the name my five year old had given him. She was sure it was a boy, and it was. We were able to see Timothy and count his tiny fingers and toes. You could hold him in the palm of your hand. This was a pro-life moment to be sure. We were all devastated. This lesson was a hard pill to swallow. As I lay on the cart in the ER that night, I stared at the crucifix before me. I felt God's presence and understood at that moment what Mary must have felt like at the foot of the cross as she gave her son back to the Father. We then released our son to his Heavenly Mother and Father, and now know that God holds him in the palm of His hand. We thank God for our faith.

I should take a moment here to tell you, that contrary to popular belief, natural family planning or FertilityCare as they call it now, is extremely reliable, safe and natural. We were not trying to get pregnant; the error was ours, not the system. NFP users must learn to appreciate their fertility together, which further enhances communication in a marriage. I was responsible for all those decisions before, and now after 15 years, we were learning a whole new way of dealing with each other and our sexuality. Instead of us controlling our fertility, we learned to let God into the picture.

I was now feeling worse than before the miscarriage. I couldn't get through the day without taking a nap. My follow-up appointment was still a month away. Then life dealt us another blow. Just a month after my miscarriage, my 35 year old sister was diagnosed with stage IV breast cancer. Her chances for recovery were slim, but for the next 18 months she battled radiation treatments, chemotherapy and a stem cell transplant. Along with her husband and three children, I was able to support her through it all. My parents were both gone, and perhaps God knew I would not be able to handle all of that, plus a new baby. However, at the beginning of her diagnosis, I questioned whether I would be able to handle it at all. I went to the doctor the next week and prayed like I've never prayed before that he would be able to help me. I was so tired and had been gaining weight. My migraines continued. I had cut down on volunteer and social activities, as I could not keep up. I went in thinking that if I was just depressed, I was ready to so some serious work. If there was something physical going on too, which I felt was the case, I asked God to help the physicians at the Institute find the best treatment for me, so that I could in turn, help my sister in her struggle. It was a difficult time for all of us, as no one really understood what was going on. Then a dear friend happened to call one morning, and I broke down and told her what I had been going through. She happened to mention that she had gone to the Pope Paul VI Institute years ago for fertility problems, and that was how she was able to have her last two children. She thought maybe they could help me. It was a God-moment for sure, and I knew I was in good hands.

We continued to chart and do blood work. My hormonal levels continued to be low, and I was diagnosed with severe PMS. I went back on the hCG shots that they had given me during my pregnancy. I also took an anti-depressant for three months until my serotonin levels returned to normal. I felt like a battery that had been re-charged. Within one month I felt amazingly better. It's funny how when you physically feel good, the difficult things in life can be managed. It was a gift. I never could have been there for my sister physically or emotionally had my health continued to deteriorate. Despite her eventual death, we had some remarkable times. The lessons learned through the deaths of those we hold dear cannot erase the pain, but when the sun shines again, we are hopefully stronger and wiser people.

Since my chances of getting breast cancer have increased by 50 percent because my sister died from it, I was led to research this ugly disease that is taking the lives of so many young women. We have much better methods of detection and treatment, but that doesn't answer the question, why. Are there many factors affecting the increase of cancer in this country? Of course, stress, environment, and genetics all play a part, but we must educate ourselves as to the growing research and connection between abortion, long term use of birth control pills and breast cancer. I will tell you that I have three teenage daughters who I've talked to about this. Two have learned to chart their cycles and one has had surgery to remove a small amount of endometriosis. She is 18 years old. Her chart mimics mine in that she has severe PMS and low progesterone and estrogen levels. They started her on hCG shots, and her levels are almost normal. Her mood swings have lessened, and my prayer is that she will not have to go through infertility, miscarriage and PMS symptoms that would continue to hurt her health and her quality of life.

Keeping a chart helps you to be pro-active, and get a jump start on trouble spots before they become major problems. Some women spend years and a lot of money on fertility treatments that many times just bring headaches. I would strongly suggest that people learn this system before they get married. They will have a much stronger, open and healthy marriage. FertilityCare is all natural, relatively inexpensive, and it works! Give it a try. That is my challenge to you. I've asked myself why I would even want to speak out on such a controversial topic. Birth control should be a personal and private matter, right? Not when the impact continues to destroy young women's health. I speak out for love of my mom, my sister, and for Timothy. Their lives had meaning and purpose. Their deaths brought me to new life, and I thank God everyday for all our blessings and the health to enjoy them.

St. Paul says, "Have no anxiety at all, but in everything, by prayer and petition, with thanksgiving, make your request known to God. Then the peace of God that surpasses all understanding will guard your hearts and minds in Christ Jesus." Philippians 4:6-7.

When God Closes One Door
He Opens Another
Donna Zoba

My name is Donna Zoba. I am 40 years old and I have been a patient of Dr. Thomas Hilgers since May of 1997. My husband, Dave, and I were married in July of 1989. As part of our marriage preparation courses, we were encouraged to attend natural family planning classes. Through our friends, Bob and Sue, we got in touch with a local Ovulation Method teacher in Southern California.

Drs. John and Evelyn Billings, of Melbourne, Australia, developed the Ovulation Method of Natural Family Planning in the early 1970s. It is on this method, that Dr. Thomas Hilgers developed the **CREIGHTON MODEL Fertility*Care*™ System**, which is now part of **NaProTECHNOLOGY.**

Dave and I attended the Ovulation Method courses prior to our marriage in July of 1989 as an alternative to using birth control, which we were totally opposed to. We were so impressed by what we learned about our times of fertility and infertility that we became Ovulation Method instructors.

From the end of 1990 to approximately 1996 we saw so much good come to the couples who took our classes. Initially couples came to our courses to avoid pregnancy, as the Ovulation Method, like the **CREIGHTON MODEL**, can be used to avoid or achieve pregnancy. What surprised us is how open couples were to God and to expanding their families when they become users of NFP. Our clients' marriages become stronger and couples became more spiritually active in their faith at church by joining various ministries.

About three years after my husband and I married, we decided it was time for us to try to achieve a pregnancy using the Ovulation Method. To this day we have not become pregnant, but the story doesn't end here, because God had other plans for us and NFP was responsible for bringing us to where we are now.

For three years we applied the Ovulation Method rules to achieve a pregnancy, until my husband, Dave, and I decided it was time for some medical intervention. As most of you reading this know, infertility techniques are big business. Due to our faith beliefs, we did not want medical intervention beyond helping our bodies work the way God intended them to work.

We saw our first reproductive endocrinologist in 1995. He wanted to start IVF procedures with us after the third month of treatment. The first couple of months he wanted us to use artificial insemination techniques, and put me on an overdose of Clomid, which a lot of reproductive endocrinologists tend to do without adequate monitoring. That initial consultation was the last time we saw him.

We continued trying to achieve a pregnancy on our own, without success. Our parish priest, Fr. Fred Gaglia, was very interested and supportive of our NFP classes. He also had a doctorate in biology. Fr. Fred knew about our frustration in not being able to become parents ourselves and he passed on a book he'd been given. The articles were written by various people who attended an NFP conference that Dr. Thomas Hilgers hosted. Dr. Hilgers also shared his breakthrough research in the field of NFP. What I learned about my infertility was an eye opener. Through the **CREIGHTON MODEL FertilityCare™ System** charting method, Dr. Hilgers was able to diagnose a host of infertility problems in women. The scary part came when my charts matched those in his book. From what I could tell, my limited mucus cycles were indicative of ovulatory dysfunction and hormonal problems.

After reading Dr. Hilgers's book, I immediately looked for a **CREIGHTON MODEL** instructor in California. We found Mary Champagne and started taking **CREIGHTON MODEL** courses from her in 1995. We learned so much from Mary, and she was a great emotional support and friend. Although Mary's dream was to have us see Dr. Hilgers for our reproductive disorders, she understood our financial and insurance concerns regarding going to Omaha, Nebraska to receive treatment. She encouraged us to find a reproductive endocrinologist in the California area first. We went about interviewing reproductive endocrinologists in our area to see how they felt about natural family planning, and how they would help couples achieve a pregnancy who use NFP. Some doctors wouldn't even talk to us, others would passively listen to us, but say that NFP was outdated, not effective, and impractical compared to all the expensive fertility measures they wanted to impose on us.

We came across one reproductive endocrinologist from San Bernardino, California. who really seemed to care, and she wanted to do a thorough infertility work-up with us before prescribing more expensive infertility procedures. David and I actually directed her efforts, using Mary's good advice.

The first procedure we had done was a Huhner's post-coital (after intercourse) test. This test showed me that my mucus was limited and Dave's sperm had mobility trouble in my mucus. Dave's seminal fluid analysis turned out fine, so that ruled out infertility problems with him. Next a blood test and ultrasound showed my hormone levels were good and I was ovulating. A laparoscopy showed that I had no evidence of endometriosis, but she did find a cyst on my left ovary, which she removed.

The next bit of advice the doctor gave us threw us for a loop. She wanted to put me on Clomid. We challenged her recommendation, because the ultrasound and hormonal tests showed I was ovulating so why put me on an ovulation-inducing drug? She really had no clear answer to our question, so we knew that we needed to find a way to make the trip to Omaha, Nebraska to become patients of Dr. Thomas Hilgers. When we told our **CREIGHTON MODEL** Practitioner, Mary, what our plans were, she was so supportive.

Mary reviewed and mailed our charts to Dr. Hilgers, and he reviewed them and wrote us a very supportive letter, stating what was next in our treatment regime. Dr. Hilgers told us that my chart showed limited mucus cycles, which were indicative of ovulatory dysfunction and hormonal abnormalities. It was such a relief to hear a clear-cut answer from him. Dr. Hilgers also said it would be necessary for me to go through a complete ultrasound series at the Pope Paul VI Institute to determine if I was ovulating, as well as a second diagnostic laparoscopy to see if I had endometriosis.

In May of 1997, I became an official patient of Dr. Hilgers. The most challenging piece about the whole infertility work-up was when I had to get my blood drawn at my local hospital every other day for one full menstrual cycle to check my hormonal levels. Since Dr. Hilgers does his own specialized testing of hormone levels at his National Hormone Lab, you should have seen the looks on the faces of the nurses taking my blood, when I said, "All I want you to do is draw my blood in a 7 cc or 10 cc red top tube, no gelatin, spin it down, and give it back to me so I can ship it myself to the National Hormone Lab in Omaha for evaluation." That caused such havoc because it was something that they didn't do or want to do. They would also ask me, "Do you have the necessary biohazard supplies? I remember the most difficult blood draw to send out was the one where Dr. Hilgers wanted to test my beta-endorphin levels. This particular blood draw had to be sent to Omaha under dry ice and there were problems with UPS. We called Linda, Dr. Hilgers's head nurse, asking her how we should ship this blood draw for testing. We followed her advice, and the shipment made it to Omaha in one piece. As I look back, we had to have a sense of humor about the whole ordeal; otherwise it would have been hard to bear.

In June of 1997, Dave and I flew from Southern California to Omaha, Nebraska for a ten-day stay so I could get a complete evaluation and my second laparoscopic procedure with Dr. Hilgers. I started the week out by going through the ultrasound series at the diagnostic ultrasound center. That place is sure state-of-the-art! My ultrasound series showed no evidence of ovulation, so this confirmed Dr. Hilgers's assessment of my charts. About the seventh day we were in Omaha, I was admitted into Bergan Mercy Hospital for my second laparoscopic procedure. Dr. Hilgers found a moderate amount of endometriosis on the outside of my uterus and ovaries, which he removed with a laser. He also performed a hysterosalpingogram during the surgery to determine if my fallopian tubes were opened. They were constricted, like the kinks you find in a water hose.

After surgery, I was put on a whole host of medications that really helped me and my well-being. I was placed on a very low dose of Clomid to induce ovulation and to improve my very low estrogen and progesterone levels. I was also put on a "wonder drug" called

Naltrexone, which stimulated and improved my beta-endorphin levels. The hormone testing had shown them to be incredibly low. Naltrexone has had a calming effect on my body, helps me to sleep and helps with my horrible PMS symptoms, mood swings, depression, as well as keeping my estrogen and progesterone levels at a normal rate. I was also put on a triestrogen suppository that stimulates mucus production and a strong dose of B[6] vitamin, which is supposed to aid women in achieving pregnancy.

After my laparoscopic procedure, Dr. Hilgers told me to continue on the drug regimen he had placed me on and if I was not pregnant within the next 12 to 16 months, to consider going back to the Institute for what one of Dr. Hilgers's nurses affectionately call the "roto-rooter" procedure. This is a major surgery where Dr. Hilgers inserts fiber optic stints inside a woman's fallopian tubes to open them up. I was a good candidate for this procedure.

In April of 1998, I went in for this major surgery, which included a C-Section incision so he could get into the reproductive organs directly to do this microscopic surgery. I was admitted into Bergan Mercy Hospital again for a weeklong stay while I recovered. During the seven-hour surgery, Dr. Hilgers also noticed that the fimbria attached themselves to my ovaries like gloves. He had to cut the fimbria into finger-like structures so they could do their job of aiding fertilized eggs up the fallopian tubes for fertilization. I was on six weeks of bed rest following surgery to recover, after which point I returned to my teaching job. I also continued on the same drug regimen and still kept trying to achieve pregnancy.

At the end of 1998 my husband was offered a job opportunity in Arizona that we couldn't pass up. From a financial perspective this would allow us the freedom to have me stop working so I could virtually relax and hopefully get pregnant. We moved to Arizona in April of 1999 with strong hopes of becoming a family. By November of 1999 we threw in the towel because we were sick of the infertility grind. We stopped trying to achieve a pregnancy, and then I decided to get off all the hormones Dr. Hilgers had me on. Boy, what a mistake! I remember the nurses telling me I would need to be on some products for hormonal maintenance but I was so distraught over not being able to become pregnant that I just wouldn't listen.

I had a hormonal withdrawal on top of the grief associated with not being able to have our own biological children. I was a literal mess! This led to getting on an antidepressant that really didn't work for me. I called the nurses at Dr. Hilgers's office and I was put back on Naltexone and hCG shots on days Peak +3,5,7 and 9 for hormonal maintenance. I am still on these medications today, and they have done wonders for me emotionally and physically.

I believe that when God closes one door, he opens another. We had started an adoption process in Arizona but didn't get to see it through to the end because Dave lost his job at the end of 2001 when the tech industry went under. Dave finally got a job in his field in March of 2003, which required us to move to North Carolina. We are finally going to realize our dream of becoming a family through adoption. We are currently working toward an International adoption from Russia and hope to have a child by Summer, 2005. It took us a long time, but we know now that it was God's will all along that we become a family through adoption.

God also knew I would need the medical expertise of Dr. Hilgers and his staff to treat my reproductive needs in the meantime. I feel better now than I have in years! Naltexone helps without the side effects that antidepressants give. Believe me, I can attest to that. Dr. Thomas Hilgers and his staff hold a very special place in my heart. Without their supportive care, love and prayers for patients, I don't know where I would be today.

PHYSICIAN'S COMMENTS:

POSTPARTUM DEPRESSION (PPD)

Thomas W. Hilgers, M.D.

After having a baby, 15 to 20 percent of women will experience some type of depressive episode. This is referred to as postpartum depression, and it can occur after a full term pregnancy or after miscarriage or tubal pregnancy. It can also occur after induced abortion.

Because of the Institute's work in Premenstrual Syndrome and the use of progesterone and hCG to stimulate progesterone production, an insight has been obtained relative to the important role of this hormone in correcting these underlying mood disorders.

Many years ago, Dr. Katerina Dalton promoted the use of progesterone as a treatment for Postpartum Depression. In the last 15 years, the Pope Paul VI Institute has implemented a program of evaluation for the use of progesterone in these circumstances. Now, it can be said, that women who suffer from Postpartum Depression, with the use of a simple treatment with the hormone, progesterone, can expect about a 95 percent recovery rate and the recovery is often very rapid.

The standard treatment for Postpartum Depression at the present time is to use antidepressants. However, this treatment takes many months and up to a year to work effectively and then never really completely works. The use of progesterone, on the other hand, can produce positive results within hours and definitely within days or weeks. It truly is a remarkable approach to this long-standing condition, and **NaProTECHNOLOGY** has allowed for it to be further evaluated and refined.

Postpartum Depression
Now Merely a Memory
Stacey Bunn

My name is Stacey Bunn, and I am 33 years old. My husband David and I have two children, Johanna (3) and Josiah (1). We have been using the **CREIGHTON MODEL FertilityCare™ System** under the guidance of Sheila St. John since we were married. We live in Salinas, California.

During my first pregnancy, I began to have some health problems that contributed to my ultimately delivering Johanna by cesarean section. Shortly after her birth, I fell into severe postpartum depression. My symptoms included extreme fatigue, lethargy, sadness, crying, fearfulness, strange and scary thoughts, and a certain distortion of my senses of hearing and seeing. I was in a sort of mental and physical fog and had little inclination to care for my baby or do much of anything else. I was able to nurse my daughter, and the importance of this to me and my husband motivated us to seek a natural remedy. After about two weeks with no improvement in my condition, we contacted Sheila. She recommended that we try a natural progesterone treatment as practiced by Dr. Thomas Hilgers of the Pope Paul VI Institute. One of our family doctors who is particularly open to natural and alternative treatments gave me an injection of natural progesterone even before we received the detailed course of treatment from Dr. Hilgers. After we established communication with Dr. Hilgers's office by phone, we proceeded with his recommended course of natural progesterone.

After about three weeks of this progesterone therapy, my postpartum depression cleared up completely, never to return. While my response to the progesterone was not as fast as some, the cure was final once my system was brought back into balance. The evidence that the progesterone was key to my recovery is strong. After one of my very first injections, I experienced one entire day free of all the negative symptoms, a miraculous recovery. This one day was a complete turnaround from the day before and the day after; I was completely myself again. And while I fell back into depression for about two more weeks, it is clear from this first positive step that the progesterone was bringing me back to normal. The other evidence of the progesterone's effect is that I recovered so completely and quickly after the three week period. Dr. Hilgers prescribed progesterone pills in this latter phase, which I took to keep my hormone levels stable.

When I became pregnant the second time with our son, we got into contact with Dr. Hilgers's office well in advance. When I was about three months along, we began to follow a plan of progesterone injections planned by Dr. Hilgers to hopefully prevent a similar bout of postpartum depression. My pregnancy went a lot more smoothly this time and I was able to deliver Josiah naturally. However, several days after his birth, I felt myself sliding into postpartum depression again. The symptoms were serious but somewhat different from the first instance. I felt horrible but was able to do more for my baby and did not experience the strange sensory fogginess that I have described above. My family and friends thought I was functioning at a higher level than the previous time, although I myself wasn't always able to appreciate this. Continuing in contact with Dr. Hilgers and his staff, I proceeded with more progesterone injections. Again, I did not respond as quickly as was hoped. But after about two and a half weeks, I again had one day of sudden and near complete recovery. I fell back into the depression, but this positive sign gave us and Dr. Hilgers enough hope to continue my course of treatment. After four weeks from the date of my son's birth, the post partum depression lifted like a dark cloud blown away by the wind, and this time it never returned.

We are extremely grateful to Dr. Hilgers and his staff for prescribing the natural progesterone therapy for us and for working closely with us over a long distance with the peculiarities and intricacies of my case. Prayer, the support of family and friends, and common sense tools like exercise and positive distractions all contributed toward alleviating my postpartum depression. But, my husband and I both believe that the natural progesterone therapy was central to my final and complete cures in both instances. Without the natural progesterone, I realize that my recovery would have taken longer, perhaps a great deal longer, and that I might have had to resort to other, more difficult and less benign, medical tools. Recovery using these other means is not only slower but can be partial and piece-meal with possible side effects. With the gift of natural progesterone therapy, my terrifying experiences of postpartum depression are now merely memories.

The Answer to Incapacitating "Baby Blues" Found
Alice Ferreira

After being married to my husband, Humberto, for two years we felt we were ready to start a family. It was the summer of 1989, and we decided to try to get pregnant. While visiting Fatima that summer, I asked Our Lady for a baby. By August of 1989 we found out we were pregnant. We were both extremely happy and excited.

For the first six months of the pregnancy I experienced severe morning sickness, accompanied by low blood pressure. Other than that, everything was normal and I was very happy. We were ready well ahead of time for the arrival of our baby. We excitedly decorated and prepared the nursery. Our baby was due to arrive on April 10, 1990, but surprised us and arrived on March 30th.

The labour and delivery were normal. I delivered quite quickly, but there were no unusual occurrences or complications. After Teresa was born we were told that she was jaundiced, but we didn't completely understand what this meant and no one explained it to us. Thus, we believed that she was sicker than she really was, having not understood what jaundice was and that it was quite common. I felt helpless at the sight of my baby under the ultraviolet lights.

By the third day of my hospital stay, depression had set in. When the morning nurse came in and asked me why I was crying, I couldn't give her an answer; I didn't know. She explained to me that I was experiencing the "baby blues" and that all mothers go through it and it would go away in a few days. At that time I was in a room by myself, and they decided to move me into a room with another new mother to see if it would help. I was feeling anxious and panicky. On the fourth day they thought that going home might help the "baby blues" to lift. So, I left Teresa at the hospital for two more days and went home to my husband and my familiar surroundings.

However, something about it all just didn't feel right to me.

Unlike other mothers who would go and spend the entire day with their baby, I would go in to the hospital to feed Teresa and then leave. When she did come home, I was happy but extremely anxious and worried that I couldn't care for her. And then she was also colicky. She would waken every hour and a half to eat and I had a hard time sleeping. Even when the baby slept, I was ultra-sensitive and hyper-vigilant to her every move or need. So, if she was sleeping I would not be able to rest for fear she would wake up as soon as I lay down, and when she was awake, I was exhausted and teary because I'd had no rest. I was feeling like I was a horrible mother.

These feelings went on for more than a week. I was able to hide them from our health nurse because I felt ashamed. But as the panic and anxiety got worse, I knew I needed to see my family doctor. The doctor tried to put me on anti-anxiety and anti-depressant medications, but they didn't work. The depression got worse. I would lie all day in bed under the blankets and hide from Teresa and her crying. Luckily, my husband, Berto, was home and able to care for her.

After a couple of days of this, Berto took me back to my doctor. She had me admitted to the hospital with Teresa. The days progressively got worse, to the point that I had planned a suicide. I felt that they would be better off without me and I would be able to stop the self-loathing and the feelings of panic. After thinking about my love for Berto and Teresa, I decided to confide in a mental health counsellor. She then informed my doctor of what was happening to me and suggested that my mother take the baby home with her for a while. I continued on in the hospital until the medication began to work, the better part of six weeks. I was also enrolled in a therapy program through mental health to help me deal with my feelings. But because I live in a small community, they didn't really know how to treat someone with postpartum depression. At one time the therapist even said that I was jealous of my baby because she was getting the attention from my parents. And I believed it because I was desperate to understand what was happening to me.

I felt that in my heart I really wanted to get close to Teresa and bond with her, but mentally all I could do was take care of her basic needs. I would go to the therapy program all day and then go to my parents and spend time bathing, feeding and holding her or going for walks; but it felt unnatural and forced. In June, my counsellor and doctor suggested that I take Teresa home one night and then return her to my parents for three nights. This rotation worked with me slowly increasing her amount of time at home, until by the beginning of August, I had her full time. I truly felt as though I didn't bond with her until she was about nine months old.

Gradually, I started to feel somewhat better. But, for many years I was terrified of becoming pregnant and going through this experience again. I remember asking my doctor what the odds would be of going through this again if I had a second child. She said that it would be higher than a normal woman because I had already had one bout of postpartum depression. I even had doctors tell me I should have my tubes tied just to prevent becoming pregnant again. But, something inside me said that I wasn't meant to have just one child. I didn't know how this would happen or when but I had faith in God that he would show me a way. I never expected it to take eight years; I thought God worked faster than that!

During a Catholic Women's League convention, I met Eileen Collins, who spoke on natural family planning. I approached her and became very interested in using this method for my own family planning. In the summer of 1997 I drove seven hours to have an introductory session and become her client. From my charting she was able to see that I suffered from premenstrual syndrome.

When I returned to my community, friends of mine found out I was using the **CREIGHTON MODEL FertilityCare™ System** and wanted me to teach them. I told them that I was not trained to do this but more and more women approached me, curious about the method, what it was, and how it worked. At this time I felt that I was experiencing a calling to a vocation, but I felt unworthy of this gift because I had used several artificial contraceptives during my marriage and knew this was against the Catholic Church's teachings. After consulting with my parish priest, he felt that I was more than worthy of this calling. So, I decided to take the **CREIGHTON MODEL** program in Omaha, Nebraska.

In October of 1997 I flew to Omaha and started my internship with the idea of also consulting Dr. Thomas Hilgers on my own case and the possibility of having another child. During my consultation with Dr. Hilgers, he informed me that he was doing a new study with natural progesterone intramuscular injections and postpartum depression. After finishing Education Phase I, I returned home and discussed with my husband the option that Dr. Hilgers had presented. After a few months of thinking and praying for guidance, we decided this was the path shown to us by God so that we would be able to add a much-wanted child to our family. In February of 1998 I became pregnant after only one month of using the method to achieve pregnancy. We were very excited but also experienced a lot of trepidation.

When I was 10 weeks gestation I went back to Omaha to Education Phase II, and Dr. Hilgers gave me the information to administer the injections and how to take blood samples and send them to the Institute. While in Omaha I also received my first injection.

When I came back to Canada I was unable to find a doctor who would administer the injections. Although they did not believe the injections would harm the baby, they didn't have enough information to feel confident in taking part. I recruited a nurse-friend to assist me with the injections, and I signed a waiver for her not to be liable. I received injections of 200 mg. intramuscularly twice a week until I was seven weeks postpartum. The pregnancy was uneventful, except for the morning sickness, which lasted only three months this time. I felt great, but my family doctor was worried and had me see him every two weeks. I had three ultrasounds because of his anxiety. Every five weeks I would have blood drawn and couriered to the Institute in Omaha to analyse my progesterone levels and tell me if I needed to increase or decrease the amount of the injection.

On November 4, 1998 at 4:13 p.m. I gave birth to my second daughter, Rebecca, weighing in at 8 pounds, 3 ounces. She was a very, healthy baby. Although I did experience some anxiety and a few panic attacks, this experience was nothing like my first. I was able to function and bond with her from the beginning. The difference this time was the support of family, friends, a wonderful therapist, and Dr. Hilgers. I don't regret anything about this experience and would do it again should we decide to have more children. I thank God for answering my prayers and leading us to Dr. Hilgers, his life's work, and the Pope Paul VI Institute.

No More Postpartum Depression
Bonnie Franzluebbers

It's been ten years since I was first diagnosed with postpartum depression. In late November 1992, I had a miscarriage 12 weeks into the pregnancy. Within two weeks I was suffering from depression, but didn't know what was happening to me. My family doctor treated me with Xanax, but I kept getting worse. By February I was admitted to the mental health center at St. Joseph's Hospital in Omaha. I was in severe postpartum depression. After a three-week stay, group talk sessions and a supply of antidepressants and other mood stabilizing drugs, I was sent home. In my opinion, these mental health centers may do a great job at treating other types of depression, but they aren't the proper treatment for postpartum depression. I felt guilty about being away from my family, and the talk sessions made me come away from them more depressed because of some of the awful circumstances others talked about enduring. I did improve over time with the treatment of the drugs; however, I didn't like the side effects and always wondered what caused me to develop such a severe case of postpartum depression.

In November 1994 I became pregnant again and delivered a healthy baby girl July 31, 1995. I had a few feelings of depression in the last couple months of the pregnancy, but fought very hard to keep them under control. After the delivery I hemorrhaged due to the placenta not properly expelling and was given five units of blood, and the doctors talked of a possible hysterectomy. I was very weak, but the bleeding subsided after a day or so. I was hospitalized away from my baby for the first three days and then re-united for two more days in the hospital. I missed my baby and I was worried about being able to breast-feed because of all the medications I had been given. I had breast-fed all four of my previous children, and it was very important to me to be able to do so.

It all went very well other than the fact that she developed thrush almost immediately after we were sent home. And the postpartum depression returned almost immediately also. I can remember being afraid to give her a bath, hold her or be alone with her. I knew I loved her, but I didn't have any feelings for her. I was just so thankful for my husband and our other children who could take care of her and love her; but again, I felt so guilty that I couldn't care for her. When she was ten days old, I had a D&C performed, because the bleeding had increased again to a heavier level. Two weeks later I was back at my family doctor, headed for severe depression again. He prescribed antidepressants and other drugs and within another month I was having a drug reaction and another three-day stay in our local hospital. I had to give up breast-feeding my baby when I went on the antidepressants, and I felt that was so unfair to both her and me.

While I was hospitalized this time, one of the nurses who knew Dr. Hilgers mentioned that she thought he had some experience with postpartum depression. I urged her to contact him, and that led to him getting in touch with my family doctor and instructing him to give me a shot of progesterone. I'm a little fuzzy on how many shots I had over the next week or two, but within a week I didn't have the severe depression symptoms, and I started to recover somewhat. My appetite started to return and I could return to work shortly after that. However, I didn't improve much from then on. My family doctor hadn't set me up to follow-up with Dr. Hilgers, so I was still taking one antidepressant and was just kind of at a standstill. I was under drug maintenance counseling and told that I would have to keep trying different ones until I found the right one. It was expensive and frustrating. We felt there had to be a better alternative. I finally pushed for my family doctor to get me an appointment with Dr. Hilgers. Finally when my baby was nine or ten months old I had completed the charting instruction and went through a series of blood tests to determine where the hormonal imbalances were. I was started on a program of monthly post-Peak progesterone injections. It was not an instant cure-all, but it got me back on the road to improving and being able to care for my family and enjoying life again. And, I didn't have to worry about all the side effects of the other types of drugs.

In February 1998 I became pregnant with our 6th child. I was in the 13th or 14th week when I again began to hemorrhage. This time the problem was due to placenta placement. My family doctor conferred with Dr. Hilgers, and increased progesterone injections were prescribed. I was hospitalized for a day and then remained in bed at home for two months until the bleeding stopped. I could then return to work on a part-time basis until our baby girl was born November 10, 1998. During the pregnancy I had progesterone injections on a regular basis, and the depression was gone. My mental state was fairly normal throughout the entire pregnancy. It was wonderful not to have to worry about all those symptoms.

After our baby was born, I continued on the progesterone injections for a time and then went to oral progesterone. I did not experience any of the negative postpartum feelings that I had with my previous child. I could breast-feed this one until she was a year old because I didn't have to take antidepressants, and I could feel my affection for her immediately. I could also feel how much I had missed out on with my previous baby's first nine months before Dr. Hilgers continually treated me. We know if we had known about this technology back in 1993, I probably wouldn't have had to experience postpartum depression to the extent that I did back then. I wouldn't have had the painful emotional experiences with my daughter's post-birth in 1995 and I wouldn't still be getting treatment in search of a total recovery.

I am not 100 percent cured of the depression, however we thank God every day for our introduction to Dr. Hilgers, the **CREIGHTON MODEL** and the technology that has helped me to this point overcome this illness. With the Institute's help and the continuing advances in **NaProTECHNOLOGY,** I hope to also continue improving to attain my normal state of health and hormonal balance.

Early Treatment of Postpartum Depression Made Huge Difference
Kathleen M. McGee

Jack Thomas McGee arrived via C-section, with lots of help from Dr. Hilgers and his staff, on a bitterly cold morning in late January 2001. Despite the cold, ice and snow, that day in January stands out as the best day of our lives. We met and fell in love with our new little son!

It had been a long and somewhat challenging pregnancy. The nausea and extreme fatigue that many women experience during the first trimester or two lasted my entire pregnancy. On top of feeling sick and tired every day, early on in the pregnancy, I was diagnosed with placenta previa. This is a condition in which the placenta partially covers the cervix and is a potentially deadly threat to both unborn child and mother.

The Institute physicians had first noticed this condition on an early ultrasound and kept an eye on my condition by ordering frequent ultrasounds. Because of the early diagnosis, bi-weekly progesterone injections, and frequent ultrasounds, Dr. Hilgers was able to accurately monitor and treat my condition, and I was able to take good care of my unborn baby and myself. Though placenta previa often causes serious problems, including heavy bleeding, I had a relatively uneventful pregnancy without even any breakthrough bleeding! To avoid any early contractions, labor, or bleeding, Dr. Hilgers scheduled a Cesarean Section for two weeks prior to my due date. We arrived at the hospital that bitterly cold morning in late January, anxiously awaiting our first meeting with our first-born child!

I spent a few days in the hospital, recuperating from the C-Section before returning home with Jack. I must say, I recovered more quickly from the C-Section than I expected. In fact, I was up walking around the day after Jack was born. Several of the nurses said that my quick recovery was due in large part to the way Dr. Hilgers performs C-

Sections. I remember one nurse commenting to me during my first walk down the hall; "Didn't you just have your C-Section yesterday? You must be a Hilgers's patient!"

The first night home with Jack went deceivingly well. He nursed well and we all got some sleep. But, day two was different. I had a hard time nursing. Panic and tears arose quickly as I worried that I could not feed my baby. At my husband's urging, I finally called my sister-in-law who had successfully nursed three children. She suggested that my breasts may be engorged and to send my husband out to buy a breast pump and formula. She assured me that Jack would be okay. My husband immediately went to the store to purchase the pump. Thankfully, the breast pump alleviated the engorgement, and I was once again able to nurse. However, I soon discovered that I was only producing about half the amount of breast milk needed each day. I was later told that this most likely was due to my "advanced maternal age" and lack of milk ducts. I was able to nurse or pump all that I could produce and then had to supplement with formula. However, I was still very grateful for the opportunity to bond with my son through breast-feeding.

Just a few days home from the hospital, I began to notice a few troublesome symptoms. Although I felt very tired, I often had trouble sleeping. I wasn't very hungry (highly unusual for me). And I was also very weepy. Not because I felt sad, but on the contrary, I felt an overwhelming sense of gratitude and love for this child, my husband, God, everyone. But the tears were always right there, on the edge. I just felt off.

I reported my observations and feelings to one of Dr. Hilgers's nurses, and she administered a questionnaire about postpartum depression. I found the questionnaire very useful. It not only helped me to identify a few other symptoms that I hadn't paid attention to, but I also felt somewhat relieved. I realized that many other new mothers had struggled with similar or worse symptoms and that Dr. Hilgers and his staff had studied the condition enough to create a questionnaire to aid in diagnosis and appropriate treatment to bring about resolution.

It turned out that my weepiness, lack of appetite and insomnia were indeed, symptoms of postpartum depression. I would not have guessed that diagnosis previous to answering the questionnaire. I had always associated postpartum with serious depressive symptoms.

As a result of being diagnosed with postpartum depression, Dr. Hilgers prescribed intramuscular injections of progesterone. Upon receiving the injections, I noticed almost immediate improvement in every area. I was better able to sleep, my appetite increased appro priately, and I felt more balanced emotionally. As with the placenta previa during my pregnancy, I believe that the early diagnosis and prompt, effective treatment of my postpartum depression made a huge difference. Had the nurses not been so knowledgeable about postpartum depression symptoms, perhaps I would have gone un-diagnosed and then developed more serious depressive symptoms later on. One can never know for sure.

I do know that my husband and I are very grateful to have such a knowledgeable and attentive doctor and staff. I have never before received such prompt, effective, woman-centered medical care. I am grateful to Dr. Hilgers and his staff for my son's life as well as my own. Early diagnosis and effective treatments of placenta previa and postpartum depression saved both.

Even Strong Women Experience Postpartum Depression
Anne M. Meers

Having a baby was supposed to be one of the best times in my life, but it ended up being one of the worst.

At the age of 26, my husband and I decided it was time to start a family. We had done everything "the right way." We both had good jobs, nice cars, owned a home, and had been married for five years. Many of our friends were beginning their families at this time also, and all of them seemed to have no trouble getting pregnant so we assumed that we would not have any problems either.

Six months of trying on our own resulted in no luck. My OB/Gyn suggested the option of a local fertility clinic. We made an appointment and got in within a few weeks. We were lucky in the fact that our insurance covered the majority of the cost for treatment, and I got pregnant from the first insemination.

My pregnancy was uneventful. I gave birth to a girl 2 ½ weeks early, but she was perfectly healthy. I felt great in the hospital and couldn't wait to get home. It seemed almost unbelievable to me that I didn't have to go back to work for 12 weeks!

The first time I thought something wasn't right was when I left my house to run an errand. As I was driving to the store, I started thinking about how great it would be to put my car in the ditch. Practicality took over, and I didn't take action on the feeling, but I couldn't rationalize why I was feeling so bad. I could list multiple reasons why I should be happy, but none why I should feel sad. I felt worthless. I didn't like my daughter or myself. I felt like everyone would be better off without me. It also seemed like these feelings became progressively worse as the days went by.

I began to live every day with dread. It took unbelievable amounts of energy to get out of bed in the morning. No matter how much sleep I had gotten the night before, I was still exhausted. I would eat a couple of crackers in the morning for breakfast, and that is all I would eat all day, as my appetite had completely vanished. I constantly wanted to be left alone. People would call and I wouldn't answer the phone and I also would not return calls from messages left on my answering machine.

Every time my daughter would make any sort of noise I would cringe. It made me very frustrated and angry just to be around her. When she would begin to cry, I would begin to cry because I didn't want to have to pick her up. I felt guilty, which in turn made me feel worse, because I didn't feel a bond with her. I also couldn't concentrate on anything. My mind seemed to be in a state of constant fuzziness, which was hard to deal with since I have always had an excellent memory.

I didn't want to leave the house, especially with my daughter. It was overwhelming to me if I was out running errands and she would cry or need her diaper changed. What should have been simple tasks to complete seemed so vast and exhausting.

One time I went with my mother and my daughter to visit my grandmother, aunt and cousins. My daughter spit up on her clothing, and that sent me into a crying spell that lasted for several hours.

I wasn't aware that there was a more severe problem than the normal "baby blues" until my mother came over to my house one day to talk to me about how I had been feeling. My mother is a nurse at Pope Paul VI Institute with Dr. Hilgers and had talked about his work for several years. Dr. Hilgers prescribed a progesterone shot and within an hour of my first shot I felt so much better that it was just unbelievable. Dr. Hilgers began to treat me with the regimen of progesterone that most of his patients are given, but I would lapse back into despair unless I received a shot every day. I eventually was receiving a shot daily, plus taking progesterone orally. I would call in daily to report to the staff how I had been feeling. At this time I also began to take Prozac. The progesterone was wonderful at keeping me feeling balanced until the Prozac had built up enough in my system to take effect. Eventually I was able to be weaned from both the shot and oral progesterone. I tried a couple of times to stop the antidepressant but have been unsuccessful in doing so.

During my recovery time, my mother and mother in-law took turns staying at our house day and night and taking care of the baby, cooking, and doing housework and anything else that I needed help with.

Before this, I never thought that depression (especially postpartum depression) was a disease. I thought that people who claimed they had experienced it were just weak. I consider myself to be a very strong person who can handle a lot of stress, and I never would have thought that I would have had a problem. Additionally, I may have been more prone to problems due to the fact that depression runs in my family. None of the other risk factors fit my situation.

I am extremely grateful for all of the help that I received from my family and especially for Dr. Hilgers's help. It is my hope that the work of Dr. Hilgers becomes more widely known and accepted so that women don't have to suffer through postpartum depression. Or, if they need additional treatment like I did, the progesterone treatment is available for use until oral antidepressants reach their full effect

PHYSICIAN'S COMMENTS:

NaProTECHNOLOGY for GENERAL HEALTH

Thomas W. Hilgers, M.D.

NaProTECHNOLOGY (Natural Procreative Technology) with the use of the **CREIGHTON MODEL System** is a far reaching, broad- based approach to women's health. While many of the more dramatic examples of its capability fall in the area of infertility, recurrent miscarriage, premenstrual syndrome and postpartum depression, it can also be used for a whole variety of other types of health issues in women of reproductive age.

These would include such things as recurrent ovarian cysts, severe dysmenorrhea (menstrual cramps), chronic pelvic pain, and abnormal bleeding of various types. In each of these cases, once the woman begins to chart her menstrual cycles, the biological markers which speak to the woman and her physician (the authentic language of the **CREIGHTON MODEL System**) and through research (the decoding of the message), we have been able to identify a whole variety of approaches to the ongoing evaluation and treatment of these conditions. In almost all cases the treatments are very effective.

Research will continue forward with the **CREIGHTON MODEL System** and **NaProTECHNOLOGY**. One area of great interest is the role of the **CREIGHTON MODEL System** in evaluating women who are at high risk to get endometrial cancer or breast cancer. In addition, there has even been new insight on the early development of osteoporosis. All of this needs to be investigated further to better understand all of the dimensions of it so that **NaProTECHNOLOGY** can offer even greater hope to the evaluation and treatment of women's health problems.

If the reader is interested, a number of Web sites can be consulted, which give even further information on the work of the **CREIGHTON MODEL Fertility***Care*™ **System**, **NaProTECHNOL-OGY** and the Pope Paul VI Institute. These include:

www.popepaulvi.com
www.naprotechnology.com
www.aafcp.org (the Web site of the
American Academy of FertilityCare Professionals).

Pain-Free Cycles Through **NaProTECHNOLOGY**
Amy Trksak

The history of my reproductive problems began after I had my first few cycles. Ever since I was 16, I associated debilitating pain with my periods. I would start to feel pain so severe that I had to lie on the floor wherever I was. I would get a high fever, so high my glasses would sometimes fog up. I'd have diarrhea, vomit, and pray through the pain. Although it lasted only about an hour, that one-hour was excruciating. There was no position where I could get more comfortable. At first, the "episodes" only happened once or twice a year. Then, by the time I was in college, it happened as often as every other cycle.

Although I was embarrassed to tell anyone about the pain, some people learned about my problem because they found me in the middle of an episode. Once, I was found by a customer on the restroom floor of the fast food restaurant where I worked as a teen. My freshman college roommate thought I was at death's door once when she found me on my bed in so much pain that I couldn't talk with her. I remember leaving church during mass once to walk the three blocks home and stopping several times because the pain blinded me and I couldn't see trees in front of me. When I finally stumbled up the stairs to my apartment, another roommate of mine was shocked to see me in so much pain. It was all I could do to say "no" when she asked if she should call 911. Needless to say, seeing me so sick, she didn't listen to me and called an ambulance to rush me to the hospital. The one good thing about these people seeing me suffer was that it encouraged me to go to the doctor.

Over the years I went to several doctors, even specialists, to explain these episodes, hoping for some relief. Some prescribed pain relief medications, but these did not relieve one bit of the pain. I distinctly remember one doctor telling me these episodes were only stress related. One thing remained the same no matter which doctor I visited, all the doctors, EVERY one I saw, recommended the Pill, and most gave me samples along with the prescription. Although I was single and saving myself for marriage, I was reluctant to take the Pill because I knew there were health risks, it wouldn't truly treat the problem, and most of all I couldn't bring myself to take something that could give a pregnant woman an abortion. I was so desperate though; I almost did take them.

When I was 28 and newly married, out of the blue I received a letter from the Pope Paul VI Institute. It began, "We received your name from a friend of yours and ours who believes you would benefit from knowing more about us..." Although I never discovered which friend gave the Institute my name, I know more than anything it was an answer to prayer. The letter described the Pope Paul VI Institute's philosophy, the problems of women they treat, and their way of treating them. As I read, I realized that some of the women the Institute helped were exactly like me; many in pain, misdiagnosed as caused by stress. I immediately recognized that here was finally a place I knew wouldn't be recommending the Pill to me. I cried when I got that letter.

I called their number that day. A short time later, I was asked to send a letter describing my symptoms, plus a small fee, any pertinent medical records, and a copy of two months of my charting. This information would allow Dr. Hilgers to give his opinion and recommendation to me regarding my next step. After Dr. Hilgers read my letter, I was thrilled that he took me as a patient. I finally had hope that my symptoms would end. After my ultrasounds, I met with Dr. Hilgers, who suspected that I had endometriosis. None of the doctors I had visited before ever mentioned even the possibility of that. The laparoscopy revealed a large amount of endometriosis. When Dr. Hilgers informed me that I would need major surgery to remove it, I actually said "good." He asked why I was glad about that. I answered that I finally had an answer and a probable solution to my problem. I was actually eager to have the date scheduled so I could possibly be rid of this pain forever!

The care I received from the Institute was top-notch. I finally felt respected and knew that someone listened to me and wanted to get to the root of my problems. I knew I wouldn't just get a pat answer, or someone telling me to try to just lower my stress levels. I was especially impressed that Dr. Hilgers scheduled the surgeries around my cycle to ensure I wasn't pregnant with a tiny baby at the time. In addition to removing the endometriosis, he also did a wedge resection on an enlarged ovary, tested my fallopian tubes to make sure they weren't plugged or damaged, and removed some cysts on my ovaries. I could completely trust him with my reproductive health.

One of the risks associated with endometriosis is infertility. Even after the surgery, Dr. Hilgers gave us a 70 percent chance of conceiving children. My husband and I prayed the Memorarae daily in hopes of conceiving a child. About four months after the surgery, using the **CREIGHTON MODEL Fertility*Care*™ System**, we learned we were pregnant! I never needed to buy a pregnancy test. It was thrilling to know my body signs that well.

Now, at age 33, I have children ages 4, 2, and newborn, and have been pain-free throughout all of my cycles since the surgery. In fact, I no longer have any of my previous symptoms. I can't say how grateful I am that the Pope Paul VI Institute exists and was able to successfully treat my illness using modern scientific methods totally acceptable by the Catholic Church (**NaPro**TECHNOLOGY). If it wasn't for the Institute I would still be in pain, and it is doubtful that any of my children would be here today. I thank God for physicians like Dr. Hilgers, who respect God's design for a woman's fertility and reproductive health.

Treatment at Institute Showed Us the Best Path
Jennifer Gaddie

Amenorrhea. It was not near so troublesome a word as other phrases I heard as I reached my teens. There was "Aunt Flo", "on the rag", and worst of all – "the curse". One of the things it seems girls enjoy discussing most is the ill fate of other young women who fall under the effects of this terrible biological event – menses. Beyond the inconvenience and the mess and the discomfort one can have, there are the surprises, the stained clothing and the embarrassment that accompanies that.

It should come as no shock that I would not be anxious to embrace that coming of age ceremony. Instead, I, under my mother's apprehensive eye, waited very patiently for menarche to pass. I must say "very patiently," for we waited until I was eighteen years old and going off to college before we became concerned enough to consult the medical field, but consult them we finally did.

My family lived overseas at the time, on an Air Force base in Germany, and we did not have the expertise at our fingertips that we might have had in America. The gynecologist I saw sent me to another base a few hours away to have an ultrasound and I recall having lab work, also. It was determined that my right ovary was "slightly enlarged", though "not abnormally so" and my testosterone was "elevated", though I did not understand any of these things. Armed with these findings, my doctor diagnosed me with polycystic ovaries and recommended I start a low-dose contraceptive to slow the rate of ovarian growth, in my right ovary particularly.

My mother had suffered similarly when she was younger, having "an orange-sized cyst" removed from her ovary in her early twenties. She did not want that in my future. Neither of us had any great knowledge beyond the limited explanation the doctor supplied. So,

I left for college and dutifully took the medication prescribed, a low-dose birth control pill and spironalactone to decrease the effects of my elevated testosterone. There was very little anxiety related to this course of action, especially to its effects on my body or my future capabilities to reproduce. My greatest anxiety was how to get my medicines refilled and sent to me from our home in Germany. I had decided to pursue a degree in nursing and for the first time began to gain some understanding of my diagnosis, in its most basic form. More importantly, I learned about the medicines I was taking, particularly the low-dose hormone. By Christmas I had discontinued the prescribed regime. Never during this time did I fear infertility, though one of my greatest desires was to have children.

When my parents moved back to the United States my second year in college, I made an appointment with another military physician at our new home. Labs were drawn, but she felt an ultrasound was unnecessary. She concurred with the diagnosis of polycystic ovaries and resumed the treatment I had discontinued earlier, reassuring me that they were the best form of treatment. When asked, she painted a slightly less attractive picture of my future fertility than my previous doctor, but I naively left her office with little apprehension. I was menstruating as long as I continued the synthetic hormones, so surely I could get pregnant somehow. I was probably the only woman my age happy to have a regular period.

I graduated from college in 1995 and my father retired from the military, moving us to Omaha, Nebraska. It was my first experience with civilian medicine and I chose an internist near our home. She was friendly and easy to talk to and I believe she was sincerely concerned with providing me with all the information she could and the best treatment she knew. However, while I was armed with a nursing degree and currently using my license in labor and delivery, I left her office each time with no more knowledge of polycystic ovaries than when I'd come and still did not experience a menses without hormonal withdrawal from the pill. I had labs drawn, but no ultrasound. She did suspect an additional diagnosis of diabetes (my blood glucose levels were in the three-hundreds), but did not suggest any treatment. Instead, she experimented with a few different types of birth control pills, suspecting them to be the cause of the elevation.

Then, the summer of 1996, I became engaged. With the date of our wedding set for the following July, I was deeply interested in discontinuing the pill. My fiancé, Greg, and I wanted to start a family as soon as we were married. We are both orthodox Catholics and believe life is sacred from conception to natural death. The awareness that oral contraceptives can be abortifacient filled us with concern and we were worried our doctor would suggest we continue it while married to keep my cycles going. We refused to do this and began looking for alternatives. The internist I was seeing recommended a prestigious gynecologist, known for her work in infertility. She reviewed the information the internist sent, I know not what, and said to come back when we "became sexually active" and were "actually trying to achieve a pregnancy". She said, "Go on your honeymoon; if you aren't pregnant in three months, come back to see me. I'll start you on a medicine called Clomid. If that doesn't work, we may need to do a laparoscopy." She made it sound so easy and hopeful.

I stopped the pill at the time suggested, one month before our wedding. Greg and I had a wonderful six weeks in Europe, where I was able to show him all the places I'd known growing up. Some of my enjoyment was stifled, however, for I was frequently nauseated in the morning, and often fatigued, and seemed to need a bathroom around every corner; each symptom building our hopes that we were pregnant. When we arrived home, we were extremely disappointed to find that not only were we not expecting a child, my menses was not starting either, and I was concerned with the symptoms as they continued to increase. I was depressed and worried, and was trying to juggle my new life with Greg with my work in labor and delivery three to four nights a week. We were disillusioned with the medical help available to us so far and could not bring ourselves to return to either doctor despite my symptoms.

It was actually the stress of my job – working nights, which led us to the Pope Paul VI Institute. My mother had seen a pamphlet from the Institute since moving to Omaha, but I could not at the time see myself as part of anyone's research – as a patient. I hoped I would have a future there as a nurse and, through God's grace, I found myself working there. To work as a nurse at the institute, I had to learn how to teach the **CREIGHTON MODEL FertilityCare™ System**, so between Thanksgiving 1997 and January 1998, I devoted myself to the initial stages of learning about women's fertility through Dr. Thomas Hilgers's program. The **CREIGHTON MODEL** gave me more information than I had ever received as a student or practicing nurse. It was here that I learned more than I could have imagined about my own body and about my diagnosis. We were introduced to **NaProTECHNOLOGY**. I underwent a complete ultrasound scan and thorough hormone testing. I had an appointment with Dr. Hilgers and he outlined what our prospects truly were. As I studied to become a FertilityCare Practitioner at the Institute, I learned to chart my fertility and I learned to interpret what I saw there. Greg and I had concrete answers for the first time.

At first we were overwhelmed and fearful. My charting showed a pattern of continuous mucus, aside from the lack of bleeding. It confirmed what we knew already: I had polycystic ovaries. I had so much mucus that, though not impossible, it was difficult to know when I might be fertile. This in itself was stressful, because we were concerned about which days to use. My ultrasounds showed what even I could see, though I'd never suspected it: my ovaries were both grossly enlarged and no longer suspended anywhere near my fallopian tubes, but hung down like over-ripe apples. My hormones were a mess.

I learned that I did indeed have diabetes, a diagnosis that explained my symptoms of fatigue, nausea and frequent urination. I started injections of natural progesterone, continuing the spironolactone. I was referred to an endocrinologist for the diabetes and began appropriate treatment for that as well.

During this journey, I completed my certification and am now a practitioner of the **CREIGHTON MODEL FertilityCare™ System**. Though my studies at college had introduced me to many encyclicals and the writings of many theologians, I had never taken the opportunity to study Pope Paul VI's encyclical, Humanae Vitae, the writing in which Dr. Hilgers received his challenge to find the answer for infertility treatment and a true method for natural family planning. Greg and I had long ago embraced its contents in our hearts, but now we gained a greater understanding of the concept of "responsible parenthood" among other truths. This became more and more important as we pursued treatment and pregnancy, together and separately. It raised questions and provided answers to many of our concerns as we pursued treatment and prayed for children.

While we quickly became comfortable with the **CREIGHTON MODEL** we were still by no means comfortable with my diagnosis. It has taken a number of years to lose the fear that had grown since our marriage – we were afraid of cancer and infertility and further problems associated with my poor ovaries. It was not an easy road emotionally. There were many "dark nights of the soul" and hours of sobbing and boxes and boxes of tissue. I experienced so much bitterness in my fear and unhappiness, even as we came to understand what was going on inside me. Now, Greg and I have passed through an ovarian wedge resection/laparoscopy in 1998 and another laparoscopy in 2000, multiple ultrasounds, hormone testing, a couple of experimental medicines – one intravenous and one oral. I used Clomid many cycles. While it did help ovulation to occur occasionally, I had a few very large painful cysts before deciding Clomid was not going to work for me. We may take it again in the future, but that is uncertain. Those of you reading this may be eagerly awaiting my "punch-line", and probably think this story will end in pregnancy. I hope you are not disappointed in **NaProTECHNOLOGY** when I tell you that we have not ever gotten pregnant. You may be wondering, my goodness, how is this a story of healing?

Greg and I used to joke that we were part of Hilgers's 20 percent failure rate. While being an impressively low rate, it is disappointing to find yourself falling in those numbers. That feeling has changed, however. We no longer consider it a terrible prospect that my body seems to be a failure. We feel it must be a part of His plan, of which we wish to embrace more fully every day. We know more about my body than we ever could have anywhere else. I learned how all of the systems in my body are related and why treating my health holistically has the most benefit for my body, instead of going by what some call the "quicker, easier route". I have gone from continuous mucus, indicating a constant state of estrogen dominance, to hardly any at all, which seems hopeful. I have recently had two menses without using hormonal withdrawal, and for that we are truly excited.

We are also more confidant in the choices we have made in pursuing pregnancy - that none of them have been an offense to God or to our marriage promises. One thing that Greg and I have always kept in our sight is that pregnancy has never been our primary goal. Having a child, for us, has never been an item on a list, something to check off like buying our first car, our first house, getting a joint account. Having a child is something we have always seen as a gift from God. I now know why I have not gotten pregnant and why I may never see that come to pass. However, it was very difficult for us to reconcile that knowledge with the unknowns, like why my body was not working as it should. It was such a big "why", a "why" that often broke my heart. We do not always get to learn why something is not happening the way we want it to. Greg and I feel blessed that God has given us one aspect of our lives to see an answer. This little "why," why aren't we able to get pregnant – we know biologically why, and even though we don't know why God allows my body to remain this way, we have peace in the little 'why', the biological reasons. During our journey, Greg and I have learned more about miracles. We have seen examples of good and bad and the outcome of both. Even as we could not have been happy conceiving a child illicitly – even though a good would come from the bad, neither would we be happy if we had miscarried a child conceived no matter how the pregnancy was achieved. Only God knows if that might have happened, but we are now at peace, realizing that God's plan is best.

We have peace knowing that I have used the knowledge presented to us through Dr. Hilgers to do what I could to further my health. I know enough now about my body and the medicines available to take those that are best for me, not simply the ones that are most convenient. Through all of that knowledge we have gained, I can be satisfied that the testing I have received is complete and reliable. All of these things give me more comfort than a pregnancy ever could have. We have recently adopted a six year old boy; a child who, everyday, shows us more of God's love for us and whom we believe epitomizes the natural unfolding of His plan. It was our medical treatment at the Institute that walked with us on this journey, not only giving us maps, but showing us the best paths to take (those wonderful scenic experiences, or the historical trips, and also those that end with a refreshing surprise) and the safest routes to bide by. It may seem blatantly obvious now, but it was our study of Humanae Vitae, that opened our hearts to the knowledge that we are not only responsible to our biological children; the children who enter our family through adoption also need healthy parents. Continuing the appropriate treatments to maintain my reproductive health is a part of how Greg and I live out "responsible parenthood" and our marriage promises.

Do we still want to conceive and bear a child of our own, biologically? Certainly, but not for the same reasons. Now we would like to achieve pregnancy simply because we are more fully aware of what miracles have to occur each time a child is conceived and carried to term and brought into the world. We would be overjoyed to be a part of that co-creation. The realization of the many miracles involved has helped us see God's will in our lives in a glorified way and lead us to a deeper appreciation, for our new son especially, but also for all of the people God has brought in and out of our lives in very special ways.

Institute Therapy has Saved My Life
Linda Schulte

At one time I considered myself to be a very normal woman. I was married in 1973, and by 1982 I had four children. Looking back on my life, there were clues telling me that my path through life was not going to be easy. I had always wanted to be a mom. To me this was one of the greatest gifts given to a woman.

You can imagine how excited I was when I became pregnant with our first child. I was extremely healthy during the pregnancy. In fact, I was healthier than at any other time in my life. However, when my first daughter was born, I became very depressed. The depression was so severe that I could hardly take care of myself, let alone feeding, bathing and caring for my daughter. We searched everywhere to find out what was causing my depression. After three months of suffering and searching, we finally found a psychiatrist who on the very first visit immediately diagnosed me with postpartum depression. He put me on an antidepressant and told me that we must live with my parents until I was better. He also told me that this depression could last from 3 to 18 months. Luckily, mine lasted six months.

My psychiatrist also told me that I could experience postpartum depression after every pregnancy and at menopause. After the depression disappeared I really wasn't afraid of becoming pregnant again. I didn't experience that same deep depression after my other three children were born. I believe that a big part of this was the constant help and care from my wonderful husband, mother and mother-in-law. Someone was with me every minute during the first six weeks after their births. They performed the cooking, cleaning, laundry, and childcare for the other children. I was responsible for only myself and my new infant.

My periods continued to be very difficult emotionally at least one or two days each cycle. I did have a miscarriage shortly after my fourth child was born. It wasn't until I reached my late 30s that other problems started to appear. I developed fibroid tumors with frequent bleeding between my periods. This diagnosis was followed by the removal of my uterus and ovaries – instant menopause. I was told that it would take one year to fully feel like myself again.

Changes seemed small at first; a pain here, a pain there. The first major pain to develop was the terrible sensation of burning in my muscles all over my body. Some days the pain grew so intense that I had trouble functioning. These symptoms seemed to multiply.

Diarrhea and constant exhaustion followed. Some days I was not even able to get out of bed. My husband worked full time and had to do my work as well. Many days I just lay in bed while my children would come in and talk with me about school, friends, etc.

My normal weight had usually been around 98 lbs., but because of the diarrhea and low appetite, I arrived at 86 lbs. I honestly felt like I was slowly dying. If I didn't get help soon, I felt that I wasn't going to make it. After many, many different doctors' appointments, I was finally diagnosed by an arthritis doctor with Fibromyalgia, Irritable Bowel Syndrome and Chronic Fatigue Syndrome. With each of these new diagnoses I was given more medications.

As my health continued to deteriorate, I was forced to leave my job of 17 years as a secretary for our church. It was one of the most difficult decisions of my life. It was the end of a very fulfilling chapter in my life.

My health condition continued to get worse. I couldn't fix supper for my family anymore. I was seeing a psychiatrist who tried several antidepressants. Each attempt was met with problem after problem. In some cases the side effects were so bad that they sent me to the emergency room for treatment. In the meantime the depression got worse and I spent more and more of my life in bed, unable to force myself to get up. I was hospitalized three times. At time, I felt like I was going out of my head. Even after the third time when I was hospitalized for nine days, I still felt very, very depressed and anxious. I was barely hanging on.

My family and I have always shared a very strong faith. It was that faith that allowed me to survive as long as I did. It was actually at a time during one of those prayerful searches that the name of Dr. Hilgers and the Pope Paul VI Institute came up. My sister-in-law was an NFP instructor and had worked with Dr. Hilgers. She recommended very strongly that I see him. Her recommendation finally offered me hope of getting better again.

As an answer to my prayers, Dr. Hilgers agreed to see me. He prescribed a series of progesterone shots in the hip. My sister offered to give me the shots. She is a registered nurse. I still felt shaky, nervous, and anxious, and my heart would pound. It wasn't until the fourth shot that I started to feel different. While I was still depressed, it was the first time that I didn't feel like I was going crazy. I even began to laugh a little. I had felt that I would never laugh again. After the fifth shot I had the best day I'd had in two years. Dr. Hilgers ran a series of tests. He checked my thyroid, DHEA, testosterone and androstenedione. All were low. My beta endorphins were 8.8 when the normal level should be 29.

My improvements were slow. Even very small accomplishments seemed very large. I started to get out of bed. I started to communicate. I was actually able to be around people. I started to take progesterone pills to replace the shots I had been given. However, with each day, I seemed to be going backwards. Dr. Hilgers had advised me to keep him informed about where I was and the direction I was going. In response to this communication, Dr. Hilgers wanted me to go back on the progesterone shots.

While I had my first hormone prescriptions filled at a pharmacy in Omaha, I asked to receive them from one locally for convenience. This ended up being a mistake. The concentrations were half the strength of those in my original prescription, so the effects were not the same. This was corrected by doubling the volume I received in my injections. My hips became swollen and bruised. I developed hard lumps deep in my hips. The pain was intense. My sister was using the normal technique of having me stand and take the weight off of one hip. In addition to my hormone treatment, I started taking Naltrexone and T_3 in the form of pills.

Rather than take a chance on receiving another incorrect prescription of progesterone at my local pharmacy, I went back to having it filled in Omaha. This change resulted in a mistake, which I soon called a miracle. With my prescription from Omaha the concentration was doubled. However, by mistake, I was given the same volume that I had been given with the weakened concentration. I felt significantly better almost immediately. Anytime I would go off my shot regimen, my severe depression would return.

With training from Dr. Hilgers's staff, my husband began administering my shots. He had me lay down on the bed because it was easier for him. He also decided to give the shot to me very slowly; taking four to five minutes to administer the injection. This helped my hips. I also began taking Vitamin E, two 400 I.U. orally, and I put the Vitamin E oil on the shot area. I didn't have as much pain, and the lumps gradually went away. Miraculously, I have been able to go further and further in-between shots.

My road to recovery has not been a straight one. I have gone from a few good days and several bad days to mostly good days and an occasional bad day. I have had terrible nightmares and still some days I wake a little depressed. Luckily, that feeling disappears once I get out of bed.

Attempts to reduce my dosage of progesterone have always resulted in a return of my previous symptoms. However, Dr. Hilgers has worked with me to keep my dosage at a level that allows me to keep my symptoms to a minimum. My husband's shot technique has allowed me to continue to get injections on a regular basis. I have been receiving these injections since May 2002.

My life is not back to where it once was, but most days I feel very good. It is a journey that I am still on. Only tomorrow will tell me what that future is. I do know the worst is over. I also know that the therapy I have received from Dr. Hilgers at the Pope Paul VI Institute has saved my life.